MW00397373

Our Birthing From Within

Keepsake Journal

by Pam England C.N.M., M.A.

Birthing From Within Books, Albuquerque, New Mexico

Acknowledgements

The *Keepsake Journal* would not have been "born" without the following people for whom I will always be grateful: first, Suzanne Palmer, who burned the midnight oil more than once in her untiring, meticulous and generous support of this project; Theodore Andrew Christiansen for his intuitive editing; and Kyle Zimmerman and Shane Harley for their creative design that makes this Journal a keepsake.

Birthing from Within Books
P.O. Box 4528
Albuquerque, New Mexico 87106
505-254-4884
www.birthingfromwithin.com

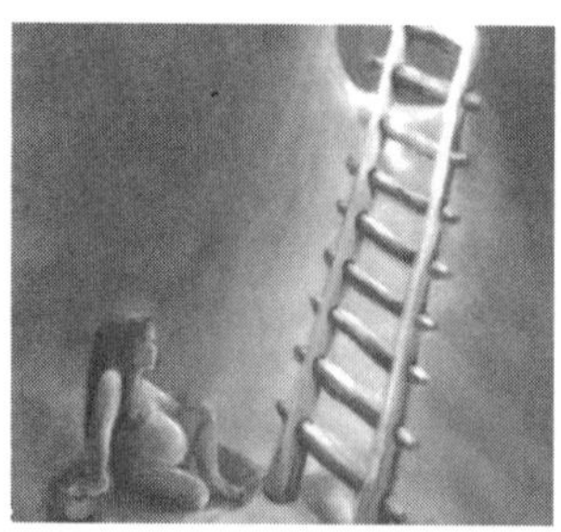

Our Birthing From Within Keepsake Journal
was written and illustrated by Pam England©2003.
Cover design by Linda Tratechaud©2003, Design Limited, Placitas, New Mexico.
Photographs by Palmer Scheutzow©2003
Book Design: Kyle Zimmerman©2003 • www.gokyle.com

England, Pam
ISBN: 0-9719102-0-0

1. Childbirth Preparation Workbook 2. Journal for Expectant Parents

Contents

Section Four: **Birth From the Father's Perspective**

Section Five: **Birth From the Baby's Perspective**

Section Six: **Birth From the Culture's Perspective**

Section Seven: **Building a Pain-Coping Mindset**

Introduction:
How to Best Use Your Keepsake Journal

Dear Parents,

What more intimate a gift could you create for your child (and grandchildren), than a living, candid and colorful chronicle of the planning, happenings, dreams and love you showered on your unborn or newly born child. Your KEEPSAKE JOURNAL, an indispensable companion designed to complement your labyrinthine journey through pregnancy and the first year postpartum, includes pages for your reflections and notes from childbirth classes. In time, this record of words, sketches/paintings, and photos will become a family heirloom-archive treasured not only by your children, but their children and grandchildren, too!

Although you can begin your JOURNAL anytime during pregnancy, if you are fortunate enough to acquire the KEEPSAKE early in pregnancy—it's best to begin with Section One. The first seven sections in your KEEPSAKE JOURNAL record your musings and learnings about birth from various perspectives (mother, father, baby and culture). Sections Eight and Nine pave the way for a gentle and conscious transition to parenthood.

Labyrinths depict the universal story of every initiatory event. Each section-page is illustrated with a womb-shaped labyrinth to portray your step-by-step journey through pregnancy, labor and birth, *and the return postpartum.* Life and birth never unfolds in a straight predictable line to achieve a certain outcome. Rather, it is labyrinthine, like this: There is only one entrance, which is also the only exit. The continuous convoluted path (unlike a maze with blind alleys), requires no prior knowledge, no thinking or planning; it only asks of us to have the faith to move forward by taking one step at a time: the path leads to the center, the goal—then leads us out again. Walking a labyrinth is not as mindless as it sounds—just as you approach the center (goal) the path takes you away on an unexpected hairpin turn—it is as perplexing and frustrating as labor and life, challenging us to choose faith over control or doubts.

Gather a pencil pouch of pencils, colored pens, magic markers, and my personal favorite: watercolor pencils, a small paintbrush and a little bottle of water—so you can work in your journal anytime and anywhere the spirit moves you. Write freely from your heart; the paper is sturdy enough for you to draw or paint directly in your journal. If you make a larger painting or a sculpture of one of the assignments, make sketch or digital photo of your birth art and paste it in your KEEPSAKE. When you draw, feel free to turn your JOURNAL in either the vertical or horizontal direction

Happy Journaling,

Pam England
December 10, 2003
Albuquerque, New Mexico

SECTION • ONE

Beginning My Journey

You can't move out unless you've moved in ...
You can't know where you are going
until you know where you are ...
and from where you came

What I Think is True about Birth

Read: ***Birthing From Within*****, pages 4-5**

Try as you might, you cannot develop a belief system or experience pregnancy or birth exclusively in a bubble of your own making. You've been learning about birth since you were a small child. Most, if not all, of what you believe about birth and parenting—as well as what you fear—was instilled in you by your entire culture long ago. To the degree assumptions and expectations go unnoticed, you are limited by them—and unconsciously live the stories and traditions you've heard.

Go up to the "mental attic" and check out all the beliefs and stories stored away in boxes and family albums. Sit quietly and alert, expectant but relaxed—just look at images, words and feelings for a moment. Whenever you're ready, take ten to fifteen minutes to write as fast as you can:

- *words, fragmented sentences, sketches or torn pictures of anything and everything you assume to be true about pregnancy, labor, birth and being a mother.*

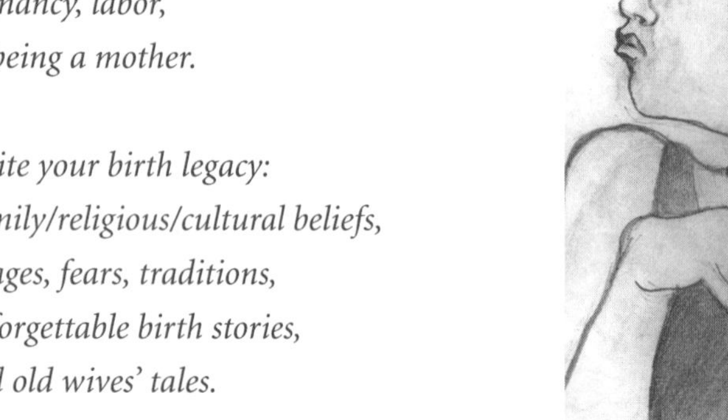

- *Write your birth legacy: family/religious/cultural beliefs, images, fears, traditions, unforgettable birth stories, and old wives' tales.*

- *Go!*

Spring cleaning your mind

date ____________________

. . . ____

____

____

____

What Do I Need to Know or Learn About?

Unlike your ancestors, you need two kinds of knowing to birth from within. The first, and most basic, is primordial knowing—the intuitive knowing in your bones (not your intellect). The second kind of knowing is modern knowing—being savvy about the hospital culture and how to birth within it. (This is equally important preparation for home-birthers in the event they do give birth in the hospital.)

- *Use these pages as an ongoing "diary" to log emerging queries and questions.*
- *Periodically check this log to guide your research and preparation for the upcoming work and transition of birth.*

date ______________

• • • ______________

From Where Am I Coming?

Read what you wrote on the previous pages aloud, or better yet, have someone read it aloud for you. Listen to your words, then journal:

- *What is the overall feeling in what you wrote?*
- *What is the theme, dominant belief or assumption expressed in your journaling?*
- *Who was your first "childbirth teacher?"*
- *What belief did he/she instill in you?*

date ____________________

. . .

What Is My Deepest Question?

Read: *Birthing From Within,* Chapter One

Knowing your personal question is central to conscious birth preparation. You might have lots of questions, but there is one deep, heartfelt question. Ask yourself, "What do I need to know to give birth as a mother?" Then…write your question:

A *living question* compels you to *live* the answer in any given moment, rather than to give wordy, intellectual explanations. If your question begs revision, don't abandon your intitial question altogether; stay with it and go deeper using the following guidelines:

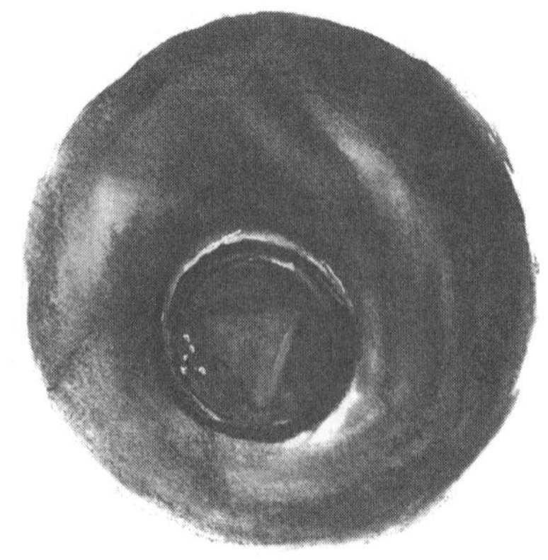

• *If your question could be answered with "Yes," "No," or "Maybe not," just get out your Crazy 8 Ball and see what it says. "Crazy 8 questions" not only leave you open to someone else answering for you, but invite images of you not doing what you really want to do. See for yourself. What images and feelings come up when you ask Crazy 8 questions? e.g., "Will I be able to handle the pain?," or "Can I avoid a cesarean?"*

• *Is your question in the future tense? For example, "How can I trust my body in labor?" Do you trust your body now? Why wait until labor? Whatever you are doing in your ordinary day-to-day life is probably what you'll do in labor—so your living question needs to be in the present tense, "How am I trusting my body now, today?"*

• *If your question could be answered by looking up the answer in a book, it's not a very deep question. For example, questions like,'"How can I be supportive in labor?" invite logical, wordy explanations. Turn this question into a living question by asking and living it this way even before labor in your everyday ordinary life: "How am I being supportive in this situation?" or "How am I bringing my love to this moment?"*

• *Is your question about changing somebody else's mind or behavior? (We keep trying that one even though we know we can't change anybody.) If your question is something like, "How can I make my doctor listen to me?," you have a question that needs revising. Word your question in such a way you could* live the answer *in many situations, e.g., "Am I willing to risk conflict to ask for what I want?" or "How can I ask this so we both 'win?'"*

IF YOU'RE NOT LIVING YOUR ANSWER NOW, YOU WON'T DO IT LATER. LATER WILL BECOME NOW, AND YOU'LL STILL NOT BE DOING IT!

Your personal question is central to conscious birth preparation. You might have lots of questions, but there is one deep, heartfelt question. Ask yourself, "What do I need to know to give birth as a mother?" Then . . . write your Living Question with a bold colored magic marker in the frame below. Write it on another 5 x 7-inch card and place it where you will see it everyday.

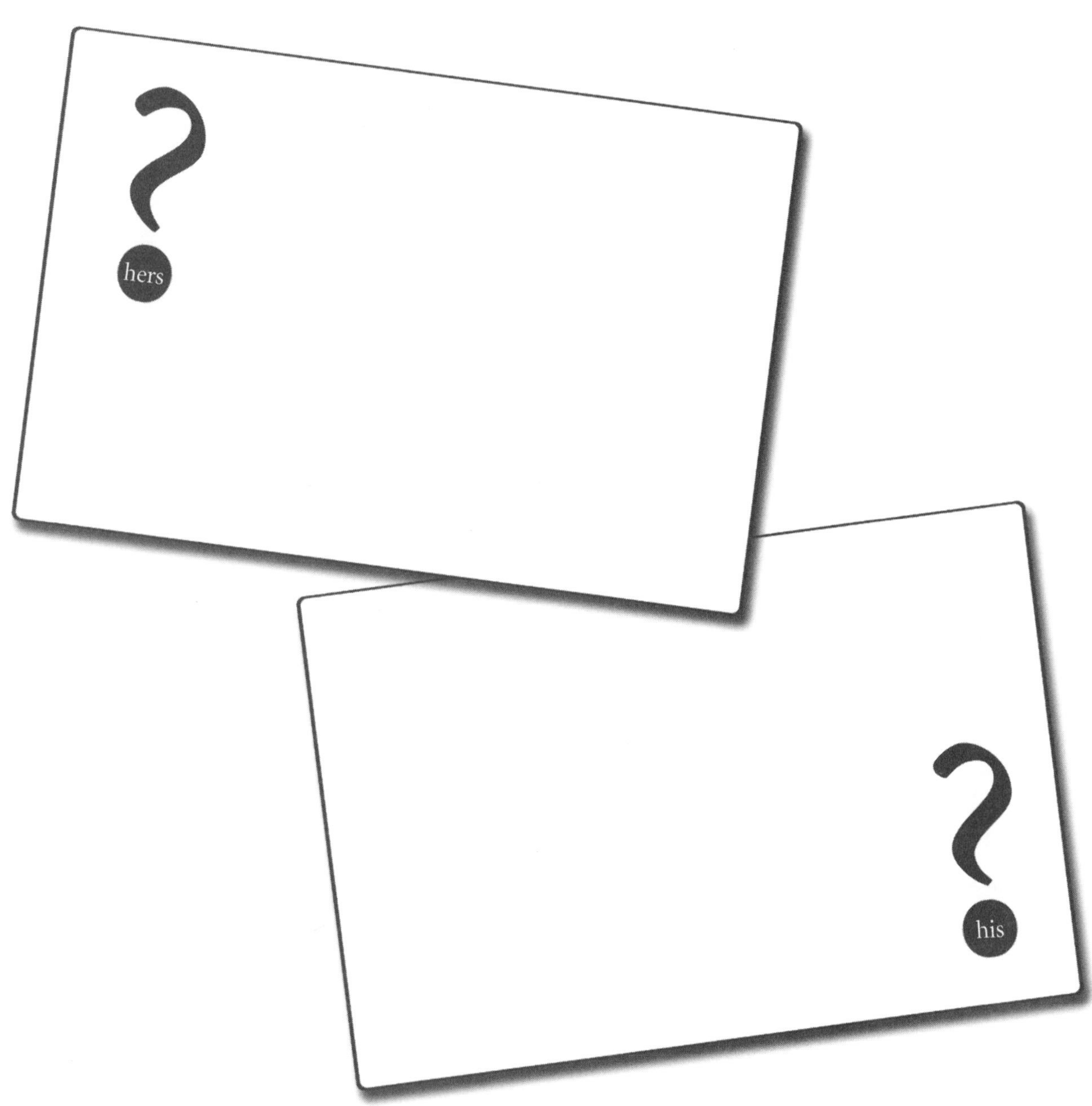

Hold your question in your heart. Ask it silently when you wake, during ordinary day-to-day activities, and as you fall asleep. Leave no stone unturned. Ask your question often and look at it from every angle until your conscious mind is exhausted and your heart is open to answers.

Living My Deepest Question

"Not asking for the answer will give you time to ponder the question."
—Veronique Vienne

Living your deepest question will form new habits of thinking and responding. Deep listening from within throughout your ordinary day will be your guide, and this kind of listening is learned through practice. Begin listening within by:

". . . attending to familiar sounds—
wind, rain, the purring of a cat,
the clatter of pots as dinner is made,
liquid pouring into a glass,
the whir of the furnace or air conditioner.

"Soon you begin to realize deep listening involves the whole body.
You hear not only with your ears,
but also with the bones of your skull
and everything linked to them."
—Jean Houston, *A Passion for the Possible*

• *Write about what is beginning to happen as you live your deepest question.*

date ____________

. . . ______________________________

"Asking your deepest question is like playing a piano
when you don't know what notes are supposed to come next.
Stop playing and listen for the answer, listen as if a distant piano were
playing the answer, but not in words."

—Marya Low • *Therapist-Shaman*
Albuquerque, New Mexico

Looking Into My Beliefs about Birth

Review the beliefs and assumptions you wrote on pages 2-5 in this Journal. Choose one that feels "negatively-charged" to you and write it here:

Whenever I identified strongly with, defended or felt righteously passionate about something, my Zen teacher, Seiju, would say quietly, "That's just your idea." That conversation stopper always turned my mind inward. In time I realized that all customs, beliefs, and assumptions are just "ideas." When you look deeply into any idea, you will ultimately find emptiness; in this space, there is no urgency to do anything. Just be. In this state, you no longer identify with the idea so you are able to be much more connected and accepting of others.

Contemplate the following questions, then write freely . . .

- *How does keeping this particular idea, assumption, or belief work for you?*
- *Who would you be if this belief or assumption were no longer absolutely true for you?*
- *What might you do differently?*
- *What if the belief dissolved altogether?*
- *Do you believe in absolute truth?*

date __________

. . .

"There is a place where I personally begin in my understanding. Although it feels true, the truth I experience is limited by my assumptions. When I let go of my assumptions, I am pleasantly surprised how much my perception and understanding expand and then allow me to see and to receive more of the truth."

—Priscilla McGee, *BFW Doula and Mentor, Washington D.C.*

Once again, review the beliefs and assumptions you wrote on pages 2-5 in this Journal. This time choose one that feels "positively-charged" to you and write it here:

Contemplate the following journaling prompts, then write freely . . .

- *Where, when, and from whom did you learn this belief?*
  - *How true is this belief?*
    - *In other words, is it absolutely true or somewhat true some of the time?*

On the surface it makes sense to grasp your "positive" beliefs with certain conviction because you feel doing so motivates or protects you in some way.

- *If that's so, how has this belief motivated you?*
  - *What do you think would happen if you no longer felt as strongly about this "positive" belief?*
    - *Are beliefs goals to be achieved?*
      - *If this belief became a preference rather than a goal to be achieved, how might you feel and what would you do differently?*

date __________

. . .

Living Practice

During conversations and in ordinary moments have fun witnessing how quickly your mind reaches back to grasp a habitual assumption or judgement, or makes a decision based on what you already know or believe, or even comes out punching in your defense. Learning to open the hand of thought doesn't come naturally; it requires devotion to the practice of allowing ideas to come and go without a white-knuckle grasp of the ones you agree with. When you think of it, you really don't need to clutch your ideas as if there is a risk of losing them; there are always more where they came from!

When you notice your mind becoming attached to a particular idea of how things or others should be—gently remind yourself, "this is just my idea." Be still and see what happens.

Commit to going beyond initial assumptions and judgements. When you go deeper and deeper into habitual beliefs, what do you know? Return often to these pages to journal breakthroughs.

Is my "mental-hand" open or clenched?

date ____________________

. . .

"The more we chase away the false certainties—those things we think we know about ourselves and others—the more mysterious our existence becomes . . . The ultimate way in which we relate to the world as something sacred is by renewing our sense of wonder."

—Sam Keen, *On the Flying Trapeze*

Connecting With My Ancestors & Women Made Wise Through Their Experience

There are unique things that only women experienced in birth can teach you about birth. Unfortunately, many women underestimate or devalue their experience and personal wisdom, and won't tell you what they know unless you ask them.

Describe the character of the sage woman sharing her understanding of birth with you. (If a wise mother is not available to you, or you don't have someone to confide in now, do this: Create a detailed mental picture of a grandmother, remembered or imaginary. Give her a name and describe her in the space below.) Then, ask her . . .

- *What is your strongest memory of giving birth?*
- *What helped you most when you gave birth?*
- *What was your spiritual experience of giving birth?*
- *What did you know after giving birth that you didn't know before?*
- *What was your first thought when you saw your baby?*
- *If you could do it over again, what would you do the same?*
- *Is there anything you would do differently?*
- *What do you wish you had known beforehand?*

date ____________________

. . . ____

My mom

Even if your relationship with your mother is not what you would have liked it to be, in becoming a mother yourself it is beneficial to connect with even the finest thread of "wholesome mothering" you experienced.

One thing my mom did that I treasure (it might have been just one time or it could have been a tradition) and that I want to continue doing with my children is:

date ____________

. . . ____________

Pregnant Woman

"A pregnant woman is a symbolic representation of motherhood, family, strength, vulnerability, femininity, and more. Very few feel neutral toward this emotionally activating symbol."
—Claudia Panuthos, *Transformation Through Birth*

- *Complete the* Birth Art Assignment *on the following page then . . .*
  - *Sit back and look at your birth art. Listen to what it is telling you. Then, write freely about whatever is coming up for you (i.e., what you are "seeing" for the first time, an emotional or physical feeling, a new question or understanding).*
    - *Refer to Appendix A for more questions that will help you learn from your birth art process.*

date ____________________

. . . ____________________

Birth Art Assignment: Pregnant Woman

Prehistoric peoples painted and sculpted hundreds of images of Pregnant Woman. Continue the tradition as you draw, paint, or sculpt your image of Pregnant Woman. Your image could be an abstraction or a human form, a self-portrait, or how you see pregnant women in general.

Eating-in-Awareness

Read: *Birthing From Within,* pages 20-27

Eating is something you do every day, so practicing eating-in-awareness is a natural way to prepare for birthing-in-awareness. The way you bring your heart and mind to ordinary day-to-day activities sets the stage for how you will be present while giving birth. So, bring your full-attention to each mundane task of meal making: buying, cleaning, cutting, chopping and mixing of the food. Silent immersion in the mundane often turns the mundane into the sacred.

Continue to be mindful when serving the meal. Years ago I was deeply moved when Mark, a quiet, unassuming student at the Sonoma Zen Center, lovingly filled my bowls with food during our silent meals. He was a living example of serving food in love and an enduring inspiration. His genuine practice of being one with the activity of serving emanated Buddha serving Buddha. In his presence, I was carried into the oneness space; only "one"—he and I, the bowl, food, and the space between us.

At least one meal a day, eat in silence without the distraction of television, music or reading material. Consider the chain of effort that went into growing, transporting, and making the food that sustains your life. Eat slowly, savor the tastes and the texture of your food. Be aware of the flavors: bitter, sour, sweet, salty, mild, and hot.

When you eat in awareness, it is likely that you will eat just the right amount, whatever that is for you. Notice the difference between eating mindfully and eating anxiously to meet daily nutritional requirements. As eating-in-awareness becomes part of your life, meeting your baby's nutritional needs will happen more naturally and pleasurably.

Leaving no traces

While preparing food, clean up as you're cooking. Use pots and utensils with gratitude and awareness; when the cooking is done, wash them, dry them and put them away. Handle each utensil, bowl, and pot quietly and with care; this will bring you into quiet mind. Clattering and banging dishes and pots interferes with your peace of mind.

Foods my baby and I crave:

date ____________

• • • ____

____

____

____

First, *many unseen laborers brought us this food; We should acknowledge how it came to us.* **Second,** *we eat this food to sustain our bodies so we may practice mindfulness as we play or work . . . and grow my baby's body.* **Third,** *as we desire the natural order of mind, to be free from clinging, we must be free from greed.* **Fourth,** *to support our life we take this food.* **Fifth,** *to live in loving-kindness, we take this food.*

—an adaptation of Zen Grace

Am I Eating Enough?

It's a good idea to check your diet during each trimester, re-visit this page every few months.

WHAT I ATE

BREAKFAST	LUNCH	DINNER
*1st check-in, date:*_________		

Contrast your diet with the **Common Sense Diet for Pregnancy** in ***Birthing From Within***, pg. 27.

I will eat more or less of these foods:

BREAKFAST	LUNCH	DINNER
*2nd check-in, date:*________		

Contrast your diet with the **Common Sense Diet for Pregnancy**.

I will eat more or less of these foods:

BREAKFAST	LUNCH	DINNER
*3rd check-in, date:*_________		

Contrast your diet with the **Common Sense Diet for Pregnancy**.

I will eat more or less of these foods:

My Prenatal Care Diary

Your midwife or doctor will be keeping medical records of your prenatal care for you, but these pages are for your home-spun prenatal record.

The day I realized I was pregnant...

The news first came to me in this way:

My first thought/feeling was:

I shared the news with:

Siblings reactions to the news:

What was happening in the world the day we knew that you were part of it:

My birth attendant(s) is/are:

I chose her/him/them because:

A word-sketch of my birth attendant(s):

Write about events like:

- *When we first heard our baby's heart beat*
- *Body changes, belly growth*
- *Insights during visits*
- *The day my baby first kicked*
- *Intuitions*

date ________________

. . .

date ______________

• • • ______________

Pregnancy & Birth-Related Dream Diary

date ____________

. . . ____________

Being Pregnant

What being pregnant or a mother means to us is defined by cultural factors. The medical culture tells you that what's important about being pregnant is all the physical changes you and the baby are going through. The media tells you what you should be feeling. Wanting to do the right thing, you may take your cues from the experts, and focus on what you *should do* and *not do*, rather than on what you know and are living.

- *Complete the* **Birth Art Assignment** *on the following page, then...*
    - *Write what came up for you when you drew this picture, or when you look at it now.*
        - *Refer to Appendix A for more questions that will help you learn from your birth art process.*

date ________________

. . . ____

Birth Art Assignment: Being Pregnant

Draw a picture that expresses what being pregnant is like for you. This could depict your physical experience, a spiritual feeling, thought or even an abstract image. Your picture can tell a whole story or just a moment in the story of being pregnant.

Our Growing Family Scrapbook

Consider including photos showing your belly growth during each trimester.

Seeing Myself as a Mother

• *Complete the* Birth Art Assignment *on the following page, then . . .*

• *Sit back and look at your birth art. Listen to what it is telling you. Then, write freely about whatever is coming up for you (i.e., what you are "seeing" for the first time, an emotional or physical feeling, a new question or understanding).*

• *Refer to Appendix A for more questions that will help you learn from your birth art.*

date ____________________

• • • ____________________

BIRTH ART ASSIGNMENT: SEEING MYSELF AS A MOTHER
Draw, paint, or sculpt what being a mother means to you.
Your image could be an abstraction or in human form.

Notes & Personal Reflections

date ____________

. . . ____________

SECTION • TWO

Preparing for Birth as a Rite of Passage

Mother Blessing, Birth Blessing

Read: *Birthing From Within,* pages 16-17

A Mother Blessing is more than a social gathering; it is an initiation ceremony designed to prepare the pregnant woman for nature's impending transformation from maiden to mother. In traditional cultures, initiates are taught "secret" practices or prayers by their elders, women made wise through their own experience. So, instead of (or in addition to) a baby shower, ask your friends and family to give you a Mother Blessing to acknowledge you and spiritually prepare you for your upcoming "birth" as a mother. Since Birth Blessings are somewhat new to our culture, you might find the following suggestions taken from ancient cultures helpful as you and your friends or family create your own.

Preparing the "Sacred Ground"

In men's rituals, "sacred ground" refers to the physical place where initiates sojourn. What and where is the sacred ground for birthing women? For pregnant women, preparation of the sacred ground is three-fold.

1. Preparation of her Physical Body

Initiates preparing for rites of passage often eat special foods, or even abstain from eating altogether; Mother Nature will create a natural fast for you in the last phase of labor. During your Blessing it is important to include a symbolic ritual of eating savory, delectable edibles, foods that symbolize strength in labor and other energies or qualities you will need to birth.

What other activities come to mind that would prepare and celebrate the body for the transformative work of labor? Consider the following:

- *Ecstatic dancing, belly dancing*
- *A deeply relaxing body or foot massage with scented oil*
- *Laughter is medicine; it massages the inner body*
- *Making and decorating a Birthin' Momma or Birth Warrior cake*
- *Painting toe nails*
- *Painting the belly*
- *Belly casting (see pages 66-68 in BFW)*
- *All ceremonies symbolically destroy one world to create a new one. From a balcony, rooftop or stairs, breaking a clay pot to symbolizes opening ourselves completely. Each participant may take a fragment home as a reminder.*

2. Opening the Inner Sanctum

A long time ago in Europe when pregnant women began to "show" or were close to term, they were often "confined"—not to bed—but from society. This solitude served the mother by allowing her time to reflect, rest, face her fears and the unknown. Society viewed this confinement as precious time for the mother to quiet her mind and to enter the sacred world before her ordeal.

It also represented the psychic and social "death" of the maiden. The temporary separation forced a visible and palpable break in the continuity of relationships, how she saw herself and how others saw her. When she returned to society after childbirth, "reborn" as a mother, she was welcomed and reintegrated as a Mother.

Regardless of where you labor physically, you will need to be at "home" psychologically and spiritually. Labor's physiological function is to open the cervix, but labor *as a rite of passage* opens the mind and heart. Before and during your Blessing, take time to "gestate" a new self-image as Wild Woman, Birth Warrior, and Mother.

If your mind begins to argue that a Blessing is a luxury you can't afford, think of it as a prenatal appointment with your soul, with the ancient ones—that your inner sanctum is a waiting room you want to spend hours in!

How will you take time to prepare your inner sanctum *before* the Blessing, before labor?

Here's a few ways to prepare your inner sanctum during the Blessing:

- *Walking silently through a labyrinth, walking in nature*
- *Sitting in a tight circle: everyone is included and can be seen, heard, and symbolically, all are equidistant from the still-point in the center from which everything turns*
- *Meditation, prayer, chanting, singing*
- *Drumming, shaking rattles and tambourines: as you concentrate mentally and physically on the rhythm, you enter a timeless, wordless state of mind that connects you to the group and to yourself. (Note: you could listen to a CD, but it's not the same as being the drummer or feeling the vibration of the drums and other instruments.)*
- *Fire gazing: fireplace, bonfire, candles*
- *Veiling yourself with a lace cover, one that drapes over your head and almost reaches the floor when you are sitting on the floor. A lace veil allows you to breathe, to see out if you need to, yet to withdraw into your inner sanctum.*

3. Preparing the Sacred Birth Space

Let there be no separation between the sacred and the profane. Bring to the home or hospital birth space, elements representing one's family, spiritual, and personal resources. One way to do this is by making a Birth Bundle (p. 41) or a receiving a Basket of Affirmations from everyone who attends the Blessing.

Here are a few ideas to get you and your friends started:

- Break a clay pot to represent opening ourselves completely
- Prepare a meal with foods that symbolize the energies or qualities you will need to birth.
- Make and decorate a Birthin' Momma or Birth Warrior Cake
- Make a belly cast
- String a birth blessing bracelet or necklace with beads representing blessings and wishes from friends
- Ask everyone to write their wish in this Keepsake Journal or a special journal

Planning My Mother Blessing

date ____________________

. . . ____________________

You might like to sing at your Blessing!

Here are lyrics to two popular songs.

Spirit [Mother; Father; Woman] am I
I am the Infinite
Within my Soul

I have no beginning
and I have no end
All this I am

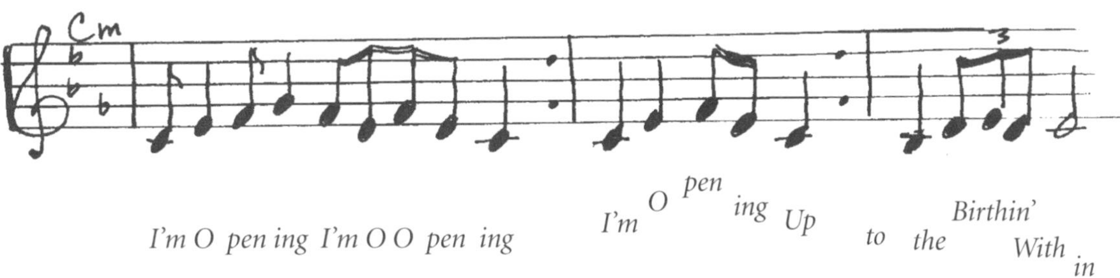
Cm
3
I'm O pen ing I'm O O pen ing
I'm O pen ing Up
to the Birthin' With in

I'm Opening
I'm Opening
I'm Opening
I'm Opening

I'm Opening Up to the
Birthin' Within
To the luminous love light
of my child
(repeat)

Memoirs of My Blessing

This is how my blessing ceremony unfolded and what gifts and insights came to me.

date ____________

. . . ____________

Birth Bundles

Making Birth Bundles is a simple but powerful ritual of preparation that acknowledges and draws upon the three energies that ideally come together during this rite of passage: mother, father, and baby. Making a Birth Bundle also acknowledges and balances another important triad of energies: the body, mind, and spirit.

Begin by choosing a piece of cloth that is large enough to hold the three special objects you will collect, and to form a "bundle" by tying the corners loosely together. The cloth can be any fabric or color, it can be bought new or be a family heirloom. One mother brought a square of satin cut from her wedding dress; another used her husband's favorite hiking bandana.

The three objects recognize and celebrate the primal energies that will arise with you in labor. The first symbol speaks to you—the Mother—reminding you of your spirituality, and your connection to the strong women in your family and all women who have ever given birth.

The second represents the energies the Father (either physically or spiritually) is bringing to this transition. Find an object that acknowledges his presence, his journey into fatherhood, or your love for one another. If you prefer, this symbol could represent the energies you will draw from your birth companions.

The third symbol will remind you that you and your baby are working as one to be born.

The search for symbolic objects activates an internal search for values and resources you will need in the labyrinth of labor. It may not be as easy as it sounds to find symbols that speak to you. Elana Burton, a Jungian psychologist and friend of mine, urges mothers not to rush or to choose a symbol that is a familiar or commercial one, unless, of course, it completely resonates with them. When you hold it in your hand, whether it is an ordinary looking rock or your grandmother's ring, it should speak to you. If it doesn't, keep looking.

When you've collected your special objects, place them on the cloth and tie it to form a bundle. Your Birth Bundle needs to be tied securely enough so it won't open until it is time to open, but loosely enough so that when it is time, it opens easily (like your cervix!).

Write about the process of discovery and what your symbols mean to you. *date* ______

• • • ______

Ceremonial Sharing of Birth Bundles

When Birth Bundles are a part of Birthing From Within childbirth classes, parents participate in a much loved *Opening of the Birth Bundles Ceremony* on the final night. If making Birth Bundles isn't part of your childbirth class, invite your midwife or friends to bear witness to the symbols and insights you gathered for your Bundle.

During this Ceremony, parents and friends sit in a close circle on the floor (it just wouldn't be the same if they were sitting in folding chairs scattered around the room). Mothers open their Birth Bundle in awareness, one at a time. Parents listen intently to one another, often swept away in laughter and tears, as each mother shares the personal meaning or stories behind the cloth

Highlights from
Opening Our Birth Bundles Ceremony Before Labor

date ____________________

. . . ____________________

Opening My Birth Bundle in Labor

Keep in mind that although a symbolic object may evoke strong feelings in you, the power is within *you*, not in the object. When you see or hold the objects in the haze of labor, they invoke an instant unspoken reminder that you are connected to all mothers throughout time and space, to your husband, birth companions and your baby—all of whom while journeying with you, simultaneously have their own journey, too. Some mothers never open their Birth Bundles in labor, but still appreciate the influence that making it had on their mindset in labor.

How my birth bundle and symbols helped me in labor . . .

date ________________

. . . ____

Laboring in a Circle of Love

"The will determines the intensity of a thought (and) the feeling behind the thought. . . If the will is strong, the thought will travel a long distance . . . For someone who is ill [or in labor] far away, it is not necessary to jump on a plane and fly over there. All you have to do is sit very quietly, go into meditation, and affirm that person's perfection...visualize the person as being completely whole, perfect, willing to do the manifestation, and immediately that person will feel it..."
–Nana Veary, Hawaiian Kahuna (Shaman)
Change We Must

Instructions For Our Candle Circle

We are inviting our family, friends and parents from our childbirth class to create a "cocoon of love" and positive energy around us while we are in labor by participating in a Candle Prayer Circle. We believe that the more prayers and the more people holding the space for us and believing in us–the better.

When we are in labor, we will call the first person/couple onour list and let them know it is time to their candle and begin the phone-chain. That person will call the person below his or her name and tell them to light their candle. Each person in turn calls the person/couple listed below him until the entire list has been called.

When you are called, light a candle. Every time you see the burning candle, or when you put it out before going to bed, you will be reminded to send another wave of love to us and envision me/us being strong in labor. Hold us, our baby and our birth attendants steadfastly in your heart and prayers throughout the day and evening.

No matter how curious you are, or how long the labor is, don't call us "check in." If we need extra support or want to give you a progress report, *we'll* call you. When our baby has been born, we (or one of our friends) will once again call the first person on the phone list to report the news, and that person will initiate the phone-chain by calling the person listed below them. Passing on the message that our baby has been born through the phone chain is equally important—if you don't make this call, candles will melt away and a lot of folks will become needlessly worried about us.

date ____________________

____

____

____

____

____

____

My Candle Circle List

NAME	PHONE	EMAIL

Notes & Personal Reflections

date ______________

. . . ______________

date ____________

• • • ____________

date ___________

• • • ___________

date ___________

• • • ___________

SECTION • THREE

Birth from the Mother's Perspective

Everything you need to know is already within you.
"oaks bear acorns, but acorns are pregnant with oaks"

Joseph Campbell

My "Strongest" Image of Labor

A good place to begin holistic preparation for birth is by exploring the images at work in your own mind. Imagined and dream images are transient, but when we find an image we like, we tend to hold on to it and quit "window shopping." Today, be receptive to whatever images of labor are in the window of your mind.

You may enjoy drawing this assignment with your partner. Later compare and discuss what you both discovered by drawing your Strongest Image of Labor.

- *Complete the* Birth Art Assignment *on the following page then . . .*

- *Sit back and look at your birth art. Listen to what it is telling you. Then, write freely about whatever is coming up for you (i.e., what you are "seeing" for the first time, an emotional or physical feeling, a new question or understanding).*

- *Refer to Appendix A for more questions that will help you learn from your birth art.*

date ____________

. . . ____

My "Strongest" Image of Labor

Close your eyes; go within. Allow images of labor and birth to move through your mind. You probably will see several images . . . notice the one that is strongest; not necessarily what being strong in labor looks like, but the most vivid or intriguing image that comes to mind when you think of birth. Notice the details, emotional or physical feelings and the sounds you are hearing. Then, draw, paint, or sculpt your Strongest Image of Labor.

Parents' Know-How in Labor

Read: ***Birthing From Within,*** **pages 120-128**

Pages for notes, practical matters and ideas that may keep my labor on track.

Ideas for our labor project:

date ________________

. . . ________________

Keeping my labor on track:

date ________________

. . . ________________

Journey Through a Labor Landscape

Birth Art Assignment: Labor as a Landscape/Journey

1. Draw or paint labor symbolically as a journey through a landscape.

2. Express the feeling, colors and all of the symbolic elements of nature and weather you imagined experiencing in the labor landscape.

3. Include yourself, anyone you may be journeying with and anything you might need to bring along.

- *Sit back and look at your Journey Through a Labor Landscape.*
  - *Listen to what it is telling you.*
    - *Then, write freely about whatever is coming up for you (i.e., what you are "seeing" for the first time, an emotional or physical feeling, a new question or understanding).*
      - *Refer to Appendix A for more questions that will help you learn from your birth art.*

date ________________

. . . ____

"To succeed on a climb one must be sure of one's goal, able to ignore the screaming revolt of muscles and lungs, and willing to accept boredom as a constant companion. . . . Rather than becoming frustrated one must adopt a Zen-like waiting, watching oneself creep upward with an objective detachment that places no premium on progress."

Ron Matous, *Quest For The Summit*

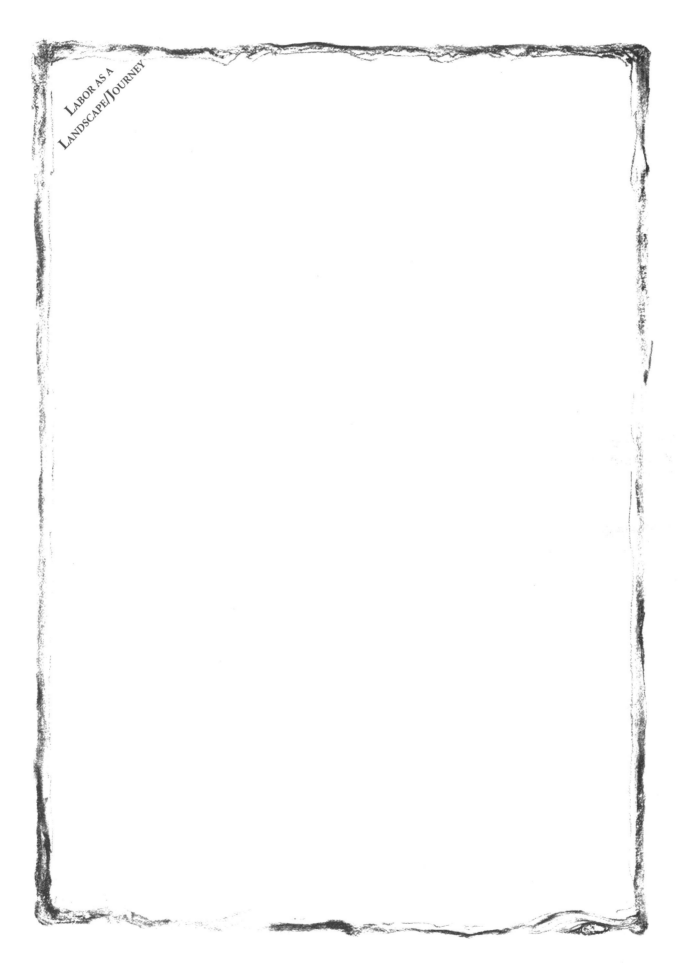
LABOR AS A
LANDSCAPE/JOURNEY

Pushing My Baby Out

Read: ***Birthing From Within,*** **pages 136-148**

• *Complete the* Birth Art Assignment *on the following page, then . . .*

Write questions or comments from your reading, what others have told you about pushing, and points you want to remember from your childbirth class.

date ________________

. . . ____

BIRTH ART ASSIGNMENT: THIS IS ME PUSHING MY BABY OUT

Draw, paint or sculpt

Birth Tiger Safari

Read: *Birthing From Within,* pages 118-119

Imagine yourself laboring in the jungle. Suppose you saw, or even thought you saw, a hungry tiger lurking in the nearby shadows. What do you think would happen to your labor?

TRACKING YOUR TIGERS

List two or three "tigers," i.e. things you hope won't happen during labor.

Choose one "tiger" you'd like to tame or cage today (you can always go on more tiger safaris later). Briefly describe your "tiger."

Let your imagination flow into your fear. Look your tiger in the eye. What are you telling yourself about this "tiger?"

Being brave means even when you are scared you keep moving anyway.

Is this fear actually happening or likely to happen, or are you fantasizing it?

Ask yourself, "What action can I take to tame or escape this tiger before labor?"

Even if you are afraid, DO IT! Get help if you need to.

The first small step I will take to tame my "tiger" is:

*If a tiger happens to cross your path in labor,
do what needs to be done to tame it
so you can get back to the work
of birthing your baby.*

Don't Be Your Own "Tiger"

Drawing On My Coping Skills

Part one: what's your tiger?

Scan your mind for something you are hoping to avoid in labor. Choose something that could happen, but not the worst possible thing you can think of.

• Once you've chosen your "tiger," let a moving image of it come up in your mental-video.

• Enlarge this image in your mind so you can really see it. It should be moving and in color (or technicolor).

• Add sound so you can hear it.

• Notice how your body feels this image . . . feel it now.

• Notice the emotions that come up.

• What are you telling yourself?

• What are you telling yourself this situation means about you? Feel *that.*

Part two:

Let yourself imagine that in spite of doing everything in your power to prevent it, what you are hoping to avoid happens. Now, instead of seeing yourself helpless in this situation, watch yourself coping in the best way you know how.

• Keep your image moving; enlarge it if you need to see in detail how you will cope best in this situation.

• Consider what you are telling yourself that helps.

• Who you are relying on to support you emotionally, physically and/or socially?

• If you like, continue with your spiritual practice.

• When you are coping, imagine how others respond differently to the situation and to you.

• You don't have to *like* the situation (when you are coping well). You still might be a little afraid, disappointed or worried; the difference is that you are resourceful and *moving* through it.

BIRTH ART ASSIGNMENT: DRAWING ON MY COPING SKILLS

Draw yourself coping with an unwished-for surprise.
Don't draw *the problem.*

Complete the Birth Art Assignment *on the previous page then . . .*

Briefly describe what you were doing, saying, and feeling in your first image, the one in which you were not coping.

When you envision yourself coping:

- *What do you see yourself doing?*
- *As a result, what is your partner, or birth attendant, doing or saying?*
- *What's the new feeling in your body?*

If you could prevent or avoid this unwished-for event, you probably would.

- *What, if anything, should you be doing now?*
- *Is anything keeping you from taking the first steps?*

Embracing Unwished-For Surprises

When you encounter circumstances you did not expect, choose or welcome, you can resist and suffer, or enter watchful and alert into the experience, utilizing your abundance of creative solutions and resources. Practice embracing unwished-for surprises in your ordinary life; journal what happens.

With genuine surrender nothing is added and nothing is "given up." Surrender means embracing and living moment-to-moment whatever is arising, and seeing Truth revealed.

date ____________________

. . . ____

"The Irish word for 'destiny,' dan, also means 'poem' and 'art.' From the same root as 'donation,' it suggests something that is given by greater than human forces, over which we have no control."
-Mara Freeman, *The Winding Knot*

A Letter to My Baby

While you wait for your baby's arrival, take a quiet moment to write down what you want to tell your baby you are feeling, hoping, and anticipating that your relationship will be. Let your baby know any special commitments you want to make in the years ahead.

Dear Baby,

Notes & Personal Reflections

SECTION • FOUR

Birth From the Father's Perspective

witnessing the mystery of birth
breathing with the mother
emerging with the baby

My Dad

Write about growing up with (or without) your dad. As an adult, are there moments when you see how your father could have been as a father if circumstances had been different for him? Write about a cherished memory, too.

date ______________

. . . ______________________________

One way I'd like to be different as a dad . . .

One thing my dad did, whether it was once or a tradition, that I want to continue doing with my child is . . .

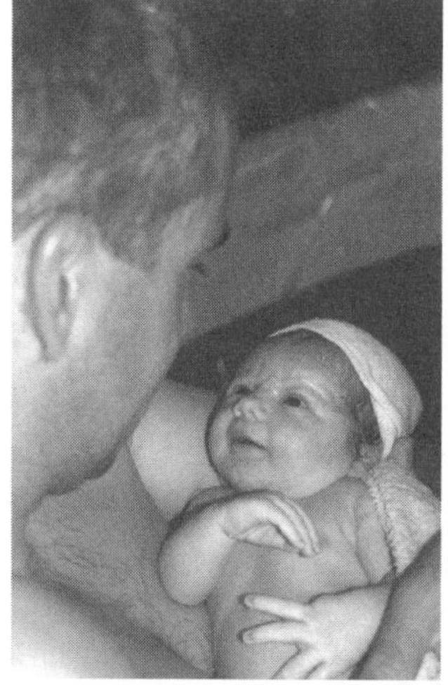
photo: Palmer Scheutzow

Seeing Myself As A Father

Becoming a father will open your heart in ways you can't fully appreciate until your baby is in your arms.

- *Complete the* BIRTH ART ASSIGNMENT *on the following page then . . .*
  - *Write what came up for when you drew this picture,or when you look at it now.*
    - *Refer to Appendix A for more questions that will helpyou learn from your birth art.*

date ________________

. . .

She is yours to hold in your cupped hands, to guard and to guide.
Give her your strength and wisdom and all the good that life can offer.
Yours is a sacred trust. Never harm her with words that can bite and sting.
Lead her into truth.
MICHELE GUINNESS, *Tapestry of Voices*

Birth art assignment: How I See Myself as a Father

Draw, paint, or sculpt an image of what being a father means to you.
Your image could be an abstraction or in human form.

My "Strongest" Image of Birth

Read: ***Birthing From Within*****, pages 52-53**

Note: *Doing this exercise with your partner can be fun; talking about your drawings may stimulate lively discussions.*

Good News: Your ability to be genuinely connected and loving during labor depends more on your mental images and expectations (of birth and your role as her labor companion) than on how much you know.

- *Complete the* BIRTH ART ASSIGNMENT *on the following page then . . .*
  - *Write what came up for when you drew this picture, or when you look at it now.*
    - *Refer to Appendix A for more questions that will help you learn from your birth art.*

date ______________

. . . ____

BIRTH ART ASSIGNMENT: MY STRONGEST IMAGE OF BIRTH
Close your eyes; go within. Allow images of labor and birth to move through your mind. You will probably see several images . . . . Notice the one that is the strongest, perhaps most vivid or intriguing. Take a good look at it, notice the details, feelings and sounds you are hearing. Then, draw this *strongest image of labor.*

Connecting With Others

Read: ***Birthing From Within,*** **pages 161-162**

Father "research" is part of expectant dad preparation. Talking with your own father and/or other men who've attended the birth of their child will give you valuable insights and strengthen your connection with other fathers.

Review the following questions. Ask and journal the fathers' responses:

- *What was most moving about the birth?*
- *What was it like to witness labor pain?*
- *What did you do that was most helpful to your wife/partner?*
- *Is there anything you wish you had known or would have done differently?*
- *Anything scary or surprising?*
- *When you first saw your baby, what was your first thought?*
- *Did you cut the cord? If so, what was that like for you?*
- *When did you realize yourself as your baby's father?* *Describe the moment or event in which you really could say* ***"I am a father!"***

date ________________

• • • ____

Notes on Labor & Birth Etiquette

Read: ***Birthing From Within,*** **pages 180-185**

When you enter the labor room bring with you an attitude of gentleness, respect, even reverence. The mother's chance of progressing well during labor improves when her birth companions preserve the body-mind harmony and protect the ecology of the birth space.

Jot down your questions and what you learn from your birth class, friends and books.

date ________________

. . . ____

photo: Palmer Scheutzow

A Pocketful of Encouragement

Fathers and birth companions often don't know what to say in labor, especially after hours of labor. If you shouldn't say "relax" or "breathe," what should you say? Ask your wife/partner to help you think of words and phrases she thinks would encourage her in labor. Then, jot down eight to ten of her favorites; arrange them in an order that would make sense as a contraction peaks and subsides.

Now, try your list out. While the mother holds ice or immerses her hand in ice water for one minute, say the phrases in the order that they are written. Speak one word or phrase about every five to six seconds until the "contraction" is over.

____

____

____

____

____

____

____

____

____

Does this work for you?

Get feedback. If necessary, change or re-arrange the order of the words or how you are saying them (i.e., speaking slower, faster, etc.). Then, try it again for three to five consecutive "ice-contractions." During the "rest" periods between contractions (lasting about a minute in this exercise), massage her lower back or feet, or simply hold the space quietly. Unless absolutely necessary, don't talk during these "rest periods"— *so she can rest body and mind.*

Talk with your wife/partner about what happened, what she experienced, when she heard the words/phrases repeated in the same order through several ice-contractions in a row.

Ask her:

- *Did you look forward to hearing the phrases?*
- *Did the phrases mark time in a helpful way? (e.g., Did she learn that a particular word coincided with the peak of the contraction, and that with the next word, the pain would be subsiding?)*
- *Do you want to change the words or the order of the words now?*

Tell her:

- *How you feel empowered or helpful as a birth companion.*

Brainstorming ideas

date ____________

• • • ____________

Copy your list and carry it in your wallet so you will be sure to have it in labor.

Phrases to help you get started:

- *Soften around the pain (or pressure/contraction/fear)*
- *You are stronger than the pain*
- *Keep going*
- *You ARE doing it*
- *I love you*
- *Breathe into it*
- *See your cervix opening*

Birth Tiger Safari

Read: *Birthing From Within,* pages 118-119

The following metaphor illustrates why it's important for you (and *everyone* who will be in the birth space for that matter), to be willing to see what could keep you from being intuitive and resourceful to your partner in labor.

Imagine you're watching a woman labor in the jungle. Suppose she saw, or even thought she saw, a hungry tiger lurking in the nearby shadows. What do you think would happen to her labor (physiologically)?

Describe any laboring mother's instinctive response to a pacing tiger?

____

____

Suppose while in labor you saw a "tiger" in labor — something that felt threatening to you as a birth companion — what would your instinctive (perhaps habitual) emotional and physiological response be?

____

____

Overwhelmed by this tiger, your confidence or ability to be supportive to the laboring mother of your child would be affected. How so?

____

____

List two or three of your birth "tigers," i.e., things you hope won't happen during labor.

____

____

Choose one "tiger" you'd like to tame or cage today: ______________________

What are you telling yourself about this "tiger?"

____

____

Is this fear actually happening, likely to happen—or are you just imagining it?

____

Let your imagination flow into your fear. Look your tiger in the eye.

Ask yourself, "What do I need to do to tame or escape this tiger?" The first small step I will take is . . .

DO IT! Do it even if you are afraid. Get help if you need to.

Now, return to your former image . . . this time see yourself encountering your now-tamed "tiger" in labor. Notice what's different this time; write what you imagine yourself doing, saying, and feeling.

Now you know how to hunt and tame your "tigers."
If during labor you meet a tiger, do what needs to be done, while abiding continuously in the Heart.

Drawing On My Coping Skills

Part one: what's your tiger?

Scan your mind for something you are hoping to avoid in labor. Choose something that could happen, but not the worst possible thing you can think of. Using a scale of 0-7, rate the "ferociousness" of your tiger — choose something below a 5.

- Once you've chosen your "tiger," let a moving image of it come up in your mental-video.
- Enlarge this image in your mind so you can really see it. It should be moving and in color (or technicolor).
- Add sound so you can hear it.
- Notice how your body feels this image . . . feel it now.
- Notice the emotions that come up.
- What are you telling yourself?
- What are you telling yourself this situation means about you? Feel *that.*

Part two:

Let yourself imagine that in spite of doing everything in your power to prevent it, what you are hoping to avoid happens. Now, instead of seeing yourself helpless in this situation, watch yourself coping in the best way you know how.

- Keep your image moving; enlarge it if you need to see in detail how you will cope best in this situation . . .
- Consider what you are telling yourself that helps . . .
- Who are you relying on to support you emotionally, physically and/or socially?
- If you like, continue with your spiritual practice . . .
- When you are coping, imagine how others respond to the situation and to you differently . . .
- You don't have to *like* the situation (when you are coping well). You still might be a little afraid, disappointed or worried; the difference is that you are resourceful and *moving* through it.

Birth art assignment: Drawing on My Coping Skills

Draw yourself coping with an unwished-for surprise.
Don't draw *the problem.*

A Letter to My Baby

While you wait for your baby's arrival, take a quiet moment to write down what you want to tell your baby you are feeling, hoping, and anticipating that your relationship will be. Let your baby know any special commitments you want to make in the years ahead.

date ______________________

Dear Baby,

Our daughter, meanwhile, was fast asleep herself,
one little hand showing above the bedclothes.
Clenched in it was my heart.

Hugo Williams

Notes & Personal Reflections

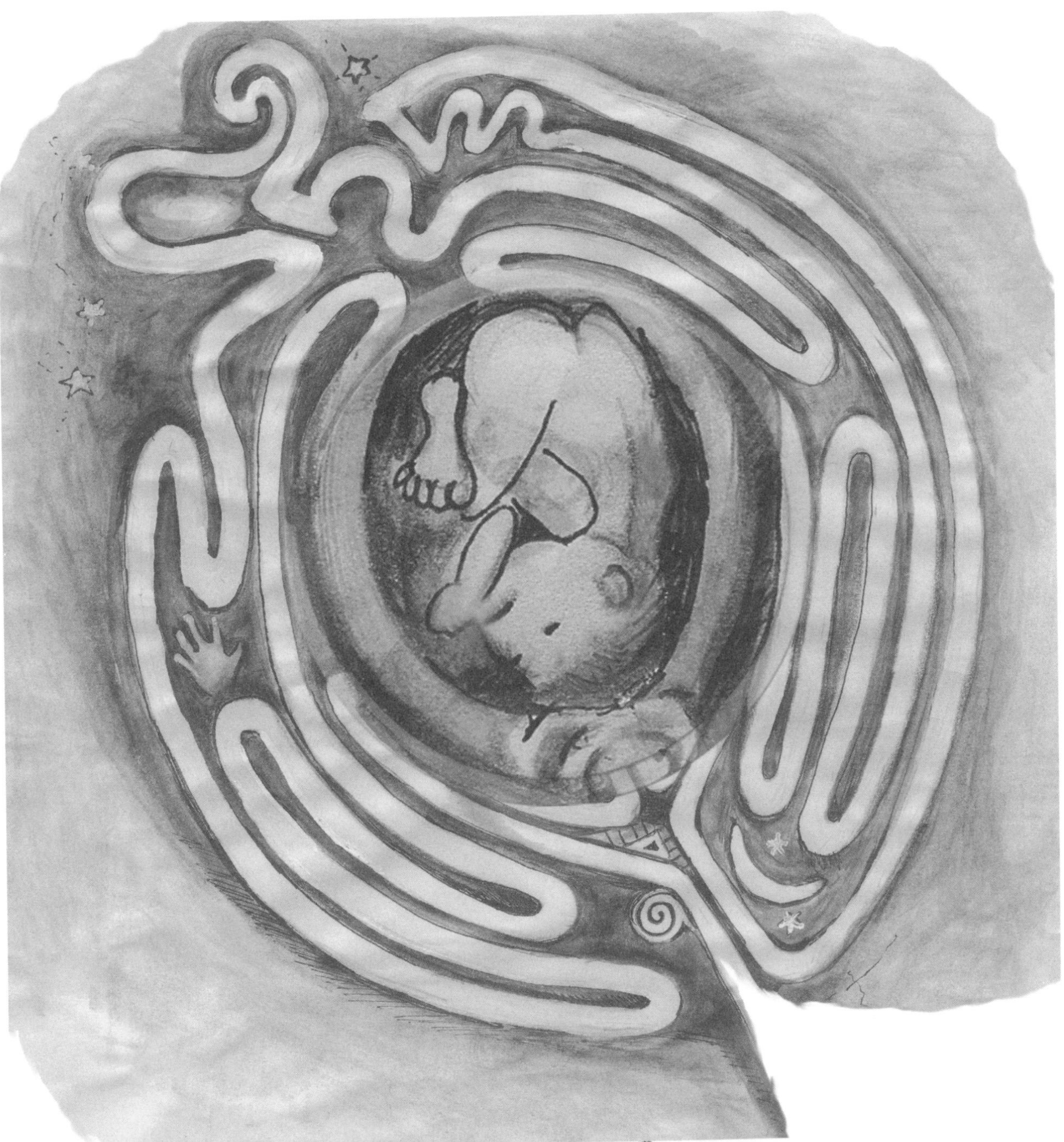

SECTION • FIVE

Birth from the Baby's Perspective

welcome your baby from its pre-conscious, wordless, meditative, dream world

Womb With a View

"I remember one mom who lived tucked away in the hills and who had suffered a life of terrible abuse. Basic amenities did not easily come her way . . . I drew a picture of a twelve-week fetus on her tummy one day. She looked and looked at it, saying not a word. Then big tears flooded her caricature, saying, 'Oh, you sweet little baby, my sweet little child. What ever do you do inside of that big house all day alone?' And then she began to laugh with delight. Her pinched face began to soften as she continued to talk to the baby, seemingly oblivious to my presence."

– Candace Fields Whitridge, *midwife*

- *Complete the* Birth Art Assignment *on the following page then . . .*
  - *Sit back and look at your birth art. Listen to what it is telling you. Then, write freely about whatever is coming up for you (i.e., what you are "seeing" for the first time, an emotional or physical feeling, a new question or understanding).*
    - *Refer to Appendix A for more questions that will help you learn from your birth art.*

date ____________

. . . ____________________________

Birth Art Assignment: Womb With a View

Imagine you could take a peek through a window in your womb. What is your baby doing in his/her womb all day? What does he/she look like? See? Hear? Feel?

As a final stroke or two, express in the drawing a personal, reassuring message you want to communicate to your baby now.

Lullabies

Your baby's ear is the first sense organ to awaken; its ears first appeared in the third week of gestation. He/she began hearing by the 16th week, and was actively listening by the 24th week. Babies learn their native language and song through listening to their parents speaking and singing—even before they're born.

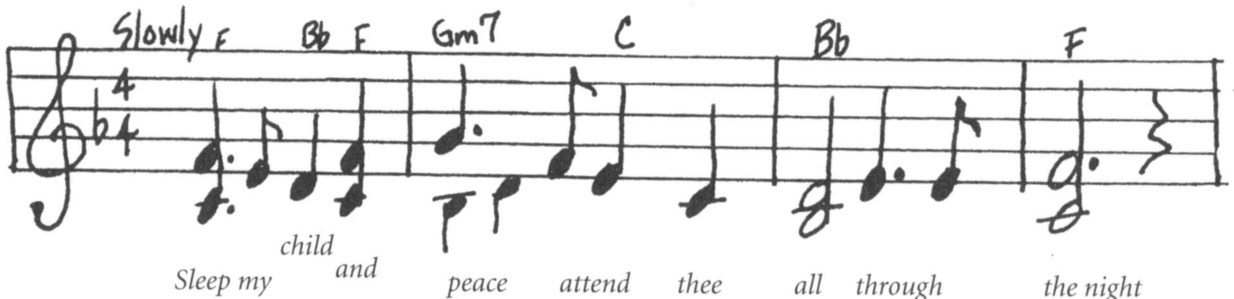
Slowly
F
Bb
F
Gm7
C
Bb
F
Sleep my child and peace attend thee all through the night

A Native American Song

Where he comes from
Nobody knows
Where he's going
Everything grows
The grass grows
The wind blows
The river flows.

Variations:
she/they (twins) / I / we

Words to my favorite lullabies

date ____________________

. . . ____

Hush little baby

I sang and read to my children, just as my mother sang and read to me. One of the songs that has bothered me as an adult is the original version of "Hush Little Baby," in which the mother buys lots of stuff to make her baby happy.

Hush little baby, don't say a word,
Mama's going to show you a hummingbird.

If that hummingbird should fly,
Mama's going to hear the crickets call.

When their sun drifts from afar,
Mama's going to search for a shooting star.

When that star has dropped from view,
Mama's going to read a book with you.

When that story has been read,
Mama's going to bring your warm bedspread.

If that quilt begins to wear,
Mama's going to find your teddy bear.

If that teddy bear won't hug,
Mama's going to catch you a lightening bug.

If that lightening bug won't glow,
Mama's going to play on her old banjo.

If that banjo's out of tune,
Mama's going to show you the harvest moon.

As that moon drifts through the sky,
Mama's going to sing you a lullaby.

Sylvia Long *Hush Little Baby,*

I'm opening up
To the
birthin' within
to the
luminous love light
of my child

— Forest Evans
A father-musician in my childbirth class

What Will Our Baby Look Like?

In 1865, an Austrian monk, Gregor Mendel, discovered the dominant and recessive patterns of passing genetic traits and resemblances from generation to generation. With billions of people on earth, no two are exactly like. Genes tell the body how to look and act; they are segments of DNA. DNA, which looks like a twisted ladder, duplicates itself to pass genes on to the next generation. Using the Mendel's basic formula, guess who, or what, your baby will look like?

Here's what you do:

First, record your (both parents) traits in the blank column , e.g., if the mother has curly black hair, under the "Mother" column write "curly black."

Then, in the "Baby" column, pen the parent's trait that is the dominant *one, or the recessive if both parents have the recessive trait.*

Sketch or color in your baby's features on the drawing. Later, you can attach a photo of your baby — for the sake of comparison.

Trait	Recessive	Dominant	Mother	Father	Baby
Hair	*blonde, red, straight*	*brown, black, curly*			
Eyelashes	*short*	*long*			
Eyebrows	*thin*	*thick*			
Eye Color	*blue*	*brown/black*			
Ears	*large*	*small*			
Earlobes	*attached*	*hanging*			
Nose	*small*	*large*			
Skin	*freckles*	*no freckles*			
Chin	*short, narrow, receding*	*normal, wide, protruding*			
Height	*tallness*	*shortness*			

Insert baby's photo here
This is what I really look like

Welcoming Our Baby

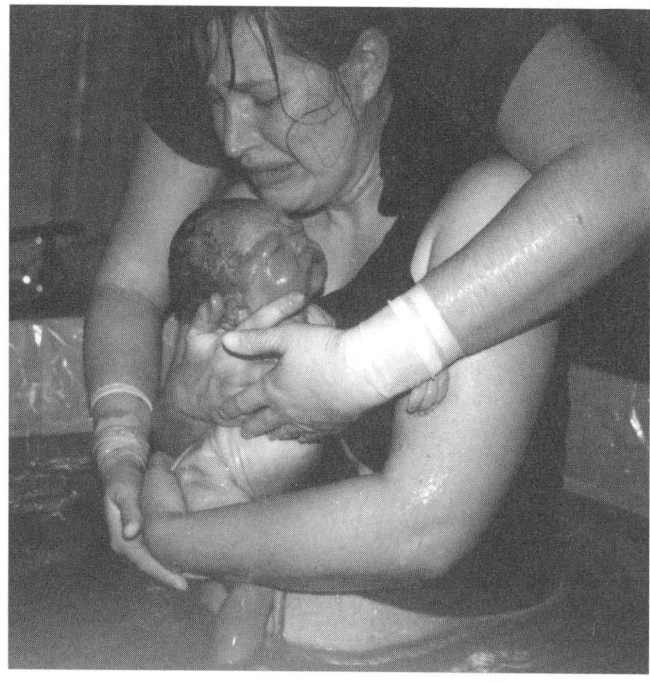

Photo: Palmer Scheutzow

"The baby is between two worlds.
On a threshold. Do not hurry.
Do not rush. Allow your baby to enter.
What an extraordinary thing
this little creature no longer a fetus,
a newborn baby. An ephemeral moment
. . . let time pass, slowly.

The baby's back has been curved
so long, curled in a ball . . . let the baby
uncoil its spine and stretch its back
at its own pace.. The arm stretches out . . .
into seemingly vast space around it . . .
The legs begin to move, to stretch,
kick into space . . .

Watch your baby breathing . . .
the chest, belly, or sides . . . the baby's
entire being is breathing in waves . . .It is
through our hands that we speak to the
child, that we communicate. Touching is
the primary language . . ."

–Frederick Leboyer,
Birth Without Violence

How will you welcome your baby?

- *Babies really need very little at birth, welcome them in peace, with hands of patience. . . and respect.*
  - *What will your hands say to your newly born baby?*
    - *What words would you have wanted to hear when you were born? What words will you softly speak or sing . . . words of welcome, or its special birth song? Will you wrap your baby in a soft blanket, one that you made?*

If circumstances arise and you can't welcome your baby in the way you've imagined immediately after birth, do it as soon as you can. Three days after my Cesarean birth, we were able to welcome Sky in our special way.

date ____________

. . . ______________________________

____

____

____

____

____

As New Parents, Learn About The Importance Of:

- *Keeping your newborn baby warm*
- *Skin-to-skin bonding*
- *Soothing, swaddling & rocking*
- *Ilotycin eye ointment*
- *Vitamin K*
- *Heel sticks (for blood sugar level and PKU)*
- *Drawbacks of the routine bath in the nursery*
- *Intact foreskin vs. circumcision*
- *Cord*

date ____________________

• • • ____________________

Where Did I Come From?

Take a moment to journal your family history or a memorable story of one of your colorful ancestors.

date ____________________

. . . ____

Creating a Family Tree

A family tree is a visual way to teach your child about his or her family history. When you draw the branches on your baby's family tree on the next page, it will uniquely represent both of your families' histories. Try sketching your family tree a few times on scratch paper until it reveals itself.

Families like trees are unique and imperfect, their growth tells a story of how they weathered their lives. Your baby's family tree will tell the story even when you aren't trying to draw it, as it did in my case. When I began sketching my family tree, I noticed that the lower branch on the father's side was always sawed off. I drew it several times, and each time that branch was missing. I asked myself why, and realized that branch represented my father, who left when I was six years old. That was interesting, and I made a short, strong branch and wrote his name in that place.

Your baby's name is recorded in the tree trunk, below the basinette, or by the ripe fallen apple.

If you're worried about making a mistake while writing on the family tree, you can write names on strips of paper or hearts and glue them on to the tree. Some people attach small photos of relatives, or write where they came from (state, country).

Family Tree

Mother's side of family

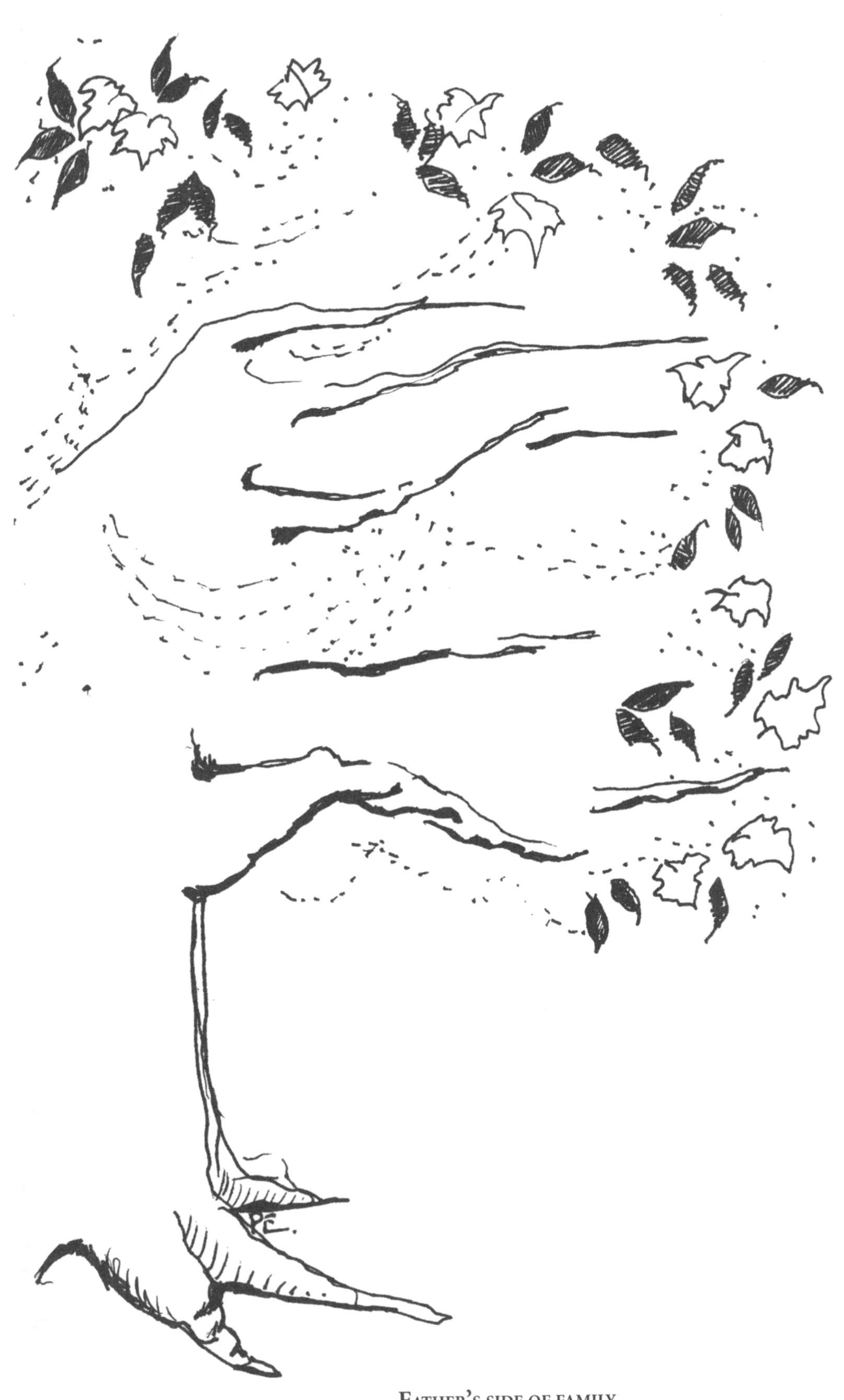

Father's side of family

Naming Our Baby

... a name is sacred and must be treated as such.

–Sobonfu Some

Where your baby comes from, nobody knows . . . but one day soon he or she will arrive naked and nameless. Choosing its name is the first and most lasting gift you will give your baby. The next could be continuing an ancient tradition of presenting the new arrival to his/her family and community through a naming ceremony.

" We are all born with at least two names. The first name maps our life purpose; the second—our last name—states our connection to mystical dimensions: animal, mineral, botanical, and so on. For instance, my last name, 'Some' means Hare. The mythical understanding of the hare is that it is the messenger of god to people. It is also the tactful one and the mediator . . .

"The belief in many African traditions is that children go through several stages before becoming full human beings. They go from the stage of pure energy—spirit—to the stage of the spirit in the human body. After the welcoming ritual at birth, the naming ritual becomes the second step of introducing the baby to the human world.

"The first time a child's name is announced to its community it must be presented in a sacred way . . . villagers wait outside while at the center of the ritual space are the elders and the grandparents. Until that day the baby's true name is not said out loud.

"After a brief ceremony, "The grandmother or grandfather whispers the baby's name three or four times, depending on the baby's sex, into the baby's ears. The name is then said out loud the same number of times. All members of the community whisper the name into the baby's ear, then give their blessings and hopes as they come down to their knees to speak to the baby."

–Sobonfu Some

- *If you know, write the legend of how you came to be named:*

date ________________

. . . ____

How We Chose Our Baby's Name

Sources of Inspiration

- *Family, ethnic or cultural names*
- *Places you've loved (like Ireland, Madrid)*
- *Names of months, seasons*
- *Gems, flowers*
- *Actors, authors*
- *Characters in books, Bible, movies*
- *A name that comes to you in a dream*

Mom's Favorite First Names and Comments:

Dad's Favorite First Names and Comments:

When choosing a middle name

Consider using mother's maiden name, the surname of an ancestor, or the first name "runner-up" and be mindful that the three initials don't spell a word, like Richard Aztec Thompson (RAT).

Mom's Favorite Middle Names and Comments:

Dad's Favorite Middle Names, Feedback and Comments:

The last name traditionally has been the father's, but new customs include matriarchal surnames, hyphenated last names or even creating a new last family-name by combining the parents surnames. (Be responsible: avoid choosing first and last names that rhyme or make a funny image.)

Any ideas?

Finalists for a girl's and boy's first, middle, and last names:

A Name Is Something To Sneeze At

In some cultures, the naming ritual allows the child to choose its own name.

> *" The tradition among the Lango tribe in Africa, for example, is for a name to be offered to the baby along with the mother's breast. If the baby refuses to drink, other names are presented until the child responds. Maori babies are dressed in feathers and held by a priest who recites a litany of ancestral names. When the baby sneezes or cries, he has announced to the family his true name."*
>
> –Pamela Redmon Satran and Linda Rosenkrantz, *The Baby Naming Journal*

What we did, who came, who was appointed as your guardian or godparents, readings, songs . . . and how you learned your name and were welcomed into our circle of family and friends.

Our naming ceremony

date ________________

. . . ____

The World

and

Your Family and Community

Welcome You

You shall be named

____

which means

____

Today,

the ________ day of ________ in the year ______

we came together to proclaim, sing, whisper your new name

Notes & Personal Reflections

date ______________

• • • ______________

SECTION • SIX

Birth from the Culture's Perspective

the positive intention of medically-focused birth customs is to ensure a safe journey

Birth In Our Culture

Birth is a universal experience, but the rituals surrounding it are remarkably different across cultures and over time. Making this drawing may help you see and explore our culture's birth customs (which you have internalized and might not otherwise see).

Complete the Birth Art Assignment *on the following page, then:*

- *Sit back and look at your birth art. Listen to what it is telling you. Then, write freely about whatever is coming up for you (i.e., what you are "seeing" for the first time, an emotional or physical feeling, a new question or understanding).*

- *Refer to Appendix A for more questions that will help you learn from your birth art.*

date __________

. . . __________

Birth in Our Culture

Imagine you are from another planet or culture. Your assignment is to send home a drawing showing what birth in this culture is like. Draw the birthplace and its customs. If there are people, show what they are doing. This may or may not represent your own birth expectations or values, but it should depict current birth customs.

Choosing Our Birth Place

Read: ***Birthing From Within*****, pages 78-85, 98-116**

Write about what you thought about when you considered "building your nest," factors that contributed to your decision, and maybe about your tour of a hospital (if you take one).

Entrainment: The Mystery of the Sacred Circuit

In 1665, Dutch scientist Christian Huygens discovered entrainment when he observed the pendulums of two clocks, mounted side by side on a wall, begin to swing together in precise rhythm "as if they wanted to keep time." Entrainment is a universal phenomenon; whenever two or more elements are in the same field, they "lock in" to achieve an energy-conserving harmony. For example, in laboratory studies when two heart cells are observed under a microscope, first beating in their own rhythm they eventually entrain one another–coming into one rhythm—and beat as one. Tribes dream together; women menstruate together. The more we move in rhythm with a person, the closer we become to that person.

It has been said "a mother gives birth alone." On one level that is true. It is also true every labor is entrained with both a seen and an unseen energy force, the collective conscious and unconscious. So, even when a mother firmly believes in her ability to give birth, if in labor she is entrained by people who fear or mistrust the process or pain of labor, or are not in alignment with her intentions (whether they verbalize their conflicting belief or not), it is possible that her (individual) mind-body-heart will be drawn into harmony with the stronger, collective rhythm.

In his book, The Science of Compassion, Gregg Braden summarizes recent research that "has now confirmed what indigenous people of the world have [known] for thousands of years. Our brain is directly linked to another vital organ in our body. Our brain is tuned to our heart. Of the sacred circuit, some say that our heart entrains the brain and our brain in turn entrains each cell of our body."

Creating a Sacred Circuit for Your Birth

List everyone who is coming to your labor/birth. Include birth attendants, and if you birth in a hospital, include labor nurses and nursery nurses.

Consider the following:

- *Does, or has, each person you've invited support and nurture you in your life?*
- *Do you feel emotionally safe and unselfconscious with each of those listed?*
- *Do you know their beliefs and attitudes about labor?*
- *Who will be called to "hold the space" for you when you are in labor—people who won't necessarily be at the birth but who will be thinking of you as you labor?*

date __________

. . .

Are your hearts beating as one?

Creating a Birth Space That Will Help Me Open

Read: ***Birthing From Within,*** **pages 98-100, 199-203**

Part one:

For this exercise, you can work exclusively in your Journal, but you may prefer a large piece of drawing paper, about 18 x 24 inches first, then make a sketch of it in your Journal. You will need magic markers.

Instructions: *First, write down four basic conditions/words that come to mind when you think of the environment a mammal typically seeks in labor, or the surroundings cave women, or most women a century or more ago, would instinctively have sought out to give birth. (Couples can work on this list together.)*

Check your answers against the answers given in Appendix B on page 268.

Next, write down four to six words that describe a birth space that you (as modern woman) imagine would make labor and birth easier for you, or that would make you feel unselfconscious, e.g., things like aromatherapy, music, names of birth companions, etc.

Finally, write down a word or two that will remind you to bring your spiritual or mindfulness practice to labor.

Using magic markers, make a "word-frame" around the edges of your paper on page 126 (words written in pastels will smudge and crayons are too difficult to read)—leave the center of the paper blank for part two of this project. If you are making this on a large piece of paper that you could hang in your birth room, write the words big enough so that you can read them easily when you are in Laborland.

Example of word frame

aromatherapy warm
space
privacy
quiet
music
dim lighting water

Part Two:
Parents appreciate and gain more insight from this exercise in their third trimester, closer to term.

If you are taking a childbirth class, your mentor or teacher may lead you in this visualization of "Opening." If you are working on your own, read the highlights of the visualization below, and use the suggestions to generate felt-images associated with opening the body-mind in labor.

The Visualization of Opening

What is the primary activity of labor, the purpose of labor?

To open!

What has to open? Most parents would say "the cervix." What else must open in labor? Your Mind . . . Heart . . . and Body . . . All of you must Open to let the baby out, to allow you to do with love and courage whatever needs to be done.

- *Open the mind . . . to all the possibilities, to the unexpected . . . and to solutions . . .*
- *Open the eyes, the inner eye . . .*
- *Open your throat . . . releasing your natural birth sounds . . . new surprising sounds...saying "yes" when you mean yes, and saying "no" when you mean no . . . asking for what you need . . . speaking words of gratitude and love . . .*
- *Open your heart . . . soften the space around your heart . . .*
- *Open your pelvis . . . soften and open the joints in front, and back . . . making more room for your baby to move down . . . and out . . .*
- *Open and soften the lower part of your great uterus . . . and your cervix—letting the baby slide down and out . . . through your soft, wet, stretchy, loose cervix...*
- *Open every cell . . . every thought, Open your entire being . . .*
- *Breathe this image and feeling of being open in body-mind-thought into every cell of your body mind . . .*

Whenever you are ready, draw your image of Opening in labor in the center of your "word frame."

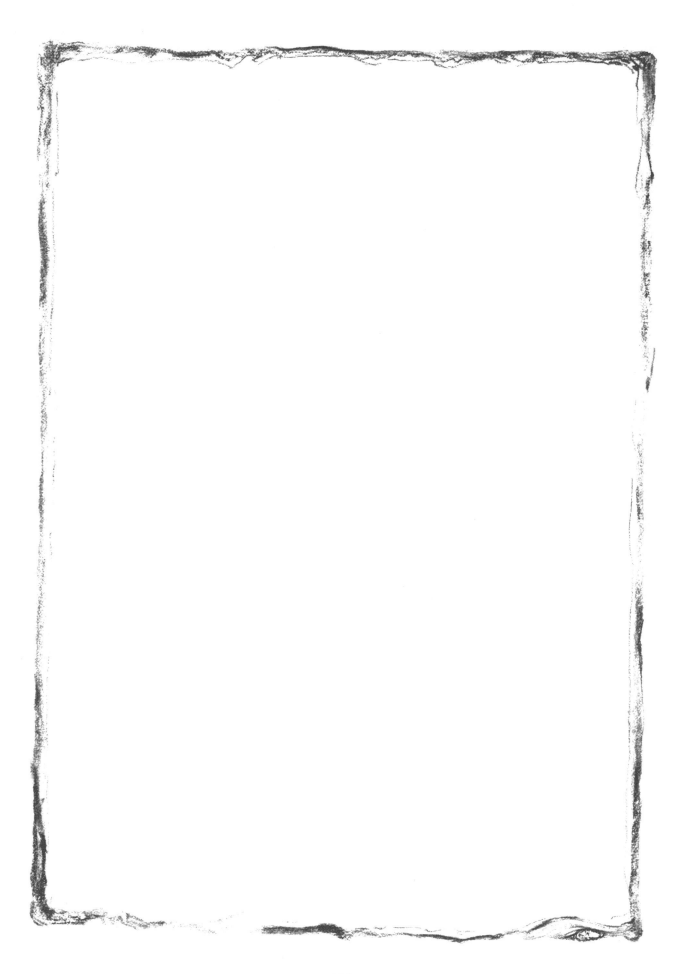

Sit back and look at your birth art. Listen to what it is telling you. Then, write freely about whatever is coming up for you (i.e., what you are "seeing" for the first time, an emotional or physical feeling, a new question or understanding).

Refer to Appendix A for more questions that will help you learn from your birth art.

Obstetrical Symbols

Read: ***Birthing From Within,*** **pages 87-88**

In this exercise, you will consider how symbols commonly found in a clinical birth place, such as the clock on the wall, a patient gown, or a wheelchair, might influence your emotions or behavior in labor.

1. In the first column on page 129, make a list of all the obstetric symbols you can think of.

2. One by one, as you visualize each obstetric symbol determine the meaning you have assigned it. Holding the image and assigned meaning in mind, notice the emotions and behavior this symbol invokes in you.

   Write the meaning, emotions and behavior invoked in the second column (see the example).

   Then, take a moment to seriously consider how this unchecked symbol could unconsciously and instantly trigger a chain-response—and without a doubt, influence your labor.

STOP

Don't read on until you've completed step 2.

3. Even when "things" (i.e., a clock, bright light) serve a purpose, and in and of themselves, they have no "meaning" or intention, individuals and whole cultures assign or adopt meanings to bring about a desired and cohesive mood or behavior.

   This is the most important step. When you see a symbol, based on your unchecked assumptions about what the symbol represents, the right-brain sends a message through your nervous system and in less than a second, you are caught in an involuntary emotional and physiological response. This immediacy can be helpful, as with traffic signs. However, in labor, you will not be able to intellectually challenge or change the meanings of obstetric symbols–before your entire physiology and mood has changed. The time to challenge your negatively-charged assumptions about obstetric symbols is NOW, so that when you see the symbol in your mind or in the real world during labor, you experience a more positive association.

   In the third column, you wll assign new "meanings" to each obstetric symbol. For example, a believable and positive association with "clock" could be "to announce the baby's birth time." During our Advanced Mentor Training (2003), a New Hampshire nurse, Donna Moore, gave new meaning to "latex gloves." "Nurses wearing gloves means that the *mother* will be the first one to touch her baby."

Step 1 Obstetric Symbols	Step 2 Meaning, emotion & behavior invoked	Step 3
Clock	*(meaning)* *hurry up, taking too long* *(emotion)* *anxiety and self-doubt that my labor is not fast enough* *(behavior)* *agree to interventions*	

Getting Information & Making Decisions

Check assumptions before consenting to or declining suggested interventions

Checking assumptions is a crucial four-step process you should include as part of your decision making process; in fact, it may be more important than asking the "right" questions.

Practice exploring assumptions, positive intentions and solution-focused planning

An Example: Imagine a healthy mother in strong labor on Friday afternoon. According to a normal labor graph, her labor is progressing a bit slowly. The birth attendant tells the parents, "We're going to break your water to speed up labor" (which in labor always sounds like a good idea!). In order for the birth attendant to have proposed breaking the water, he or she must have either made an accurate assessment or a general assumption about this mom's labor. Go within and try to imagine the birth attendant's assumptions, the parent's assumptions, their positive intentions and propose a solution-focused plan.

My assumption of the birth attendant's motivation to break the water: ______________________

(e.g. They were hurrying her because it's late on Friday; Labor is going too slowly; They must know 'cause they're the trained experts)

I imagine the birth attendant believes: ______________________

(e.g. Labor is going too slowly; Following labor graphs and offering early intervention is the best management; Labor won't be strong enough on its own.)

I assume the BA's positive intention is: ______________________

(e.g. To shorten labor and decrease additional interventions; To augment labor that she believes is already too long; To assess the baby's well-being by checking for meconium in the amniotic water.)

What needs to be learned or done next? Ask the birth attendant: ______________________

(e.g. Is this labor abnormally long?; How is it a medical problem for the mom or baby?; You know a lot of ways to get labor going—what else can we try first?)

Now, consent to or decline the procedure

If you are still undecided, it is your right and responsibility to get more information or a second opinion.

Four steps to checking assumptions

1. After listening to the birth attendant's proposal, infer the underlying assumption.

2. Consider your birth attendant's *positive intention* **for your well-being in suggesting the intervention.**

3. With this in mind, clarify the birth attendant's unspoken assumption or belief by asking him or her to explain his or her reasoning, and anything else you need to know more about. (Don't assume your assumption about the assumption is accurate.)

4. Check your own assumptions before you make your decision. If you are inclined to automatically refuse something, what is your underlying assumption?

date ______________

• • • ______________

Cartoon Role Plays

Making Allowances for Our Assumptions —

Mine: ______________________________

Theirs: ______________________________

Propose BA's positive intention:

____

What do I need to ask or do next?

(Write your answer in the blank bubble.)

____

Making Allowances for Our Assumptions —

Mine: ______________________________

Theirs: ______________________________

Propose BA's positive intention:

____

What do I need to ask or do next?

____

Making Allowances for Our Assumptions —

Mine: ______________________________

Theirs: ______________________________

Propose BA's positive intention:

____

What do I need to ask or do next?

____

Making Allowances for Our Assumptions —

Mine: ________________________________

Theirs: ________________________________

Propose BA's positive intention:

____

What do I need to ask or do next?

____

Making Allowances for Our Assumptions —

Mine: ________________________________

Theirs: ________________________________

Propose BA's positive intention:

____

What do I need to ask or do next?

____

Making Allowances for Our Assumptions —

Mine: ________________________________

Theirs: ________________________________

Propose BA's positive intention:

____

What do I need to ask or do next?

____

Having the Courage to Do the Next Best Thing

Developing a mindset and the confidence and determination to *do the next best thing* (in labor or life) takes real guts. It is not about controlling events or others.

Doing the next best thing begins in the mental posture of being fully open, alert, facing what is put before you and daring to look at it, listen to it, touch it and let it touch you. Rather than being defeated by unwished-for surprises or telling yourself stories about how it should be—rise up and embrace what is before you. It means you whole-heartedly respond to the labor that is unfolding.

date ________________

. . . ________________

Notes & Personal Reflections

date ____________

. . . ____________

SECTION • SEVEN

Building a Pain-Coping Mindset

Labor hurts , it's hard work and you can do it.

—Suzanne Stalls, CNM
Albuquerque

How I Picture Labor Pain

Do this exercise *before* you begin practicing BFW pain-coping practices. (There are two frames on the next page so both parents can do this exercise.)

Birth Art Assignment

Take just a minute to draw the first image that comes to mind of labor pain, or coping with pain, in one of the frames. Be honest. Draw a line, shape, symbol or a realistic representation. (Use pastels or markers.)

Make a quick note about your image, then turn the page and begin building a pain-coping mindset.

date ____________________

• • • ____________________

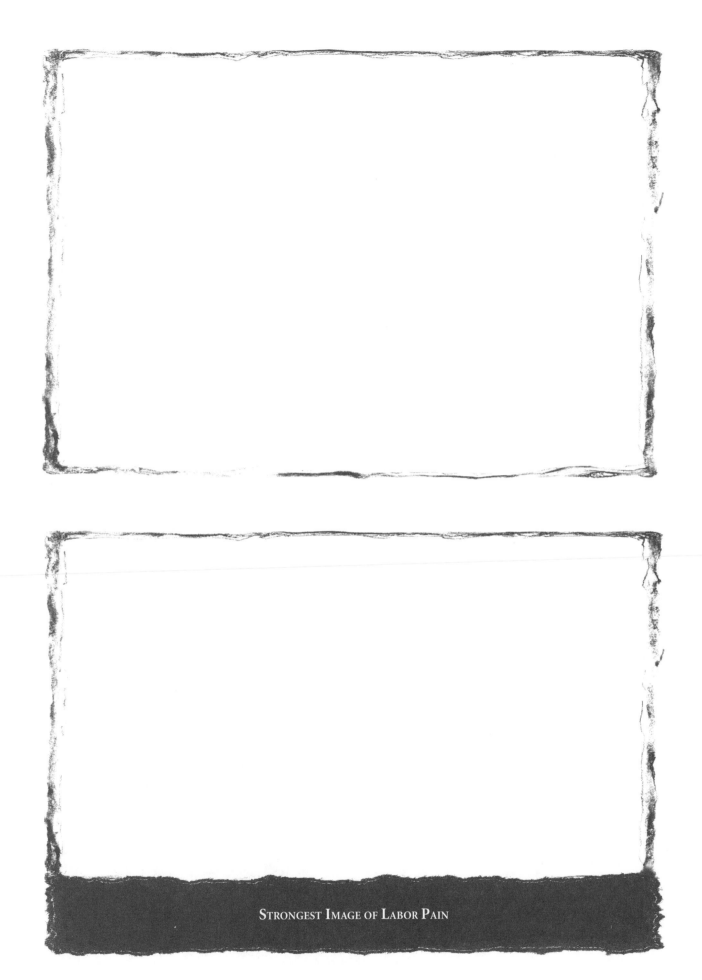

Strongest Image of Labor Pain

Birthing Through Pain

Read: *Birthing From Within*, pages 190-212

In addition to learning pain-coping practices, parents who birthed through pain in-awareness suggest expectant parents do the following.

- *Explore beliefs and attitudes, your own and those of everyone in your birth space; consider how they might influence your experience of pain.*
- *Mindfully choose and entrain your birth companions and the birth space.*
- *Create a birth space that will help you move through labor.*
- *Practice pain-coping practices until they become automatic.*
- *Differentiate pain from suffering.*
- *Immerse yourself in your spiritual practice or positive thinking.*

date ________________

• • • ____

____

____

____

____

____

____

____

____

"Pity is the experience of meeting pain with fear. It makes one want to change the givens of the moment . . . But when we touch the same pain with love, letting it be as it is, meeting it with mercy instead of fear and hatred, then that is compassion."

–Stephen Levine

photo: Palmer Scheutzow

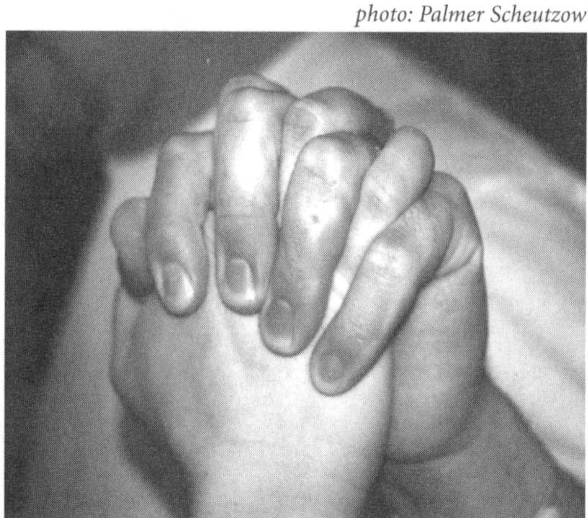

The Art of Breathing

Birds do it. Bees do it. We do it. We exhale and release into the atmosphere carbon dioxide, a chemical that promotes the growth of plants . . . when we empty our lungs, we help make the grass grow greener.

For some reason, in our culture, there is a lot more emphasis on inhaling than on exhaling. While we associate taking in oxygen with doing something useful and good for ourselves, we expel carbon dioxide surreptitiously, almost as if we were taking out the garbage—in a rush, nose pinched, mouth open. Always on the uptake, we derive almost no pleasure from relaxing our chests, clearing our airways, and sending forth some colorless CO into the blue yonder.

To breathe deeply and effortlessly, don't wait to exhale. Think of breathing as giving, not taking. Just tell yourself that you are going to fill up your lungs in order to expel as much air as possible. Don't scrimp. Dole out an ample supply of carbon dioxide. Picture in your mind one of your favorite trees and give its leaves a chance to produce some grade-A, top quality oxygen.

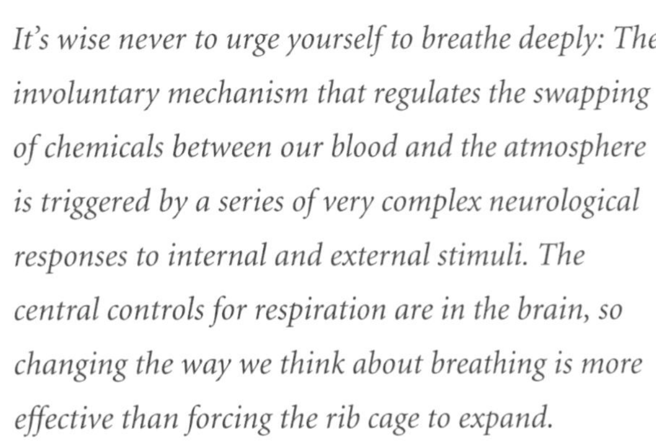

It's wise never to urge yourself to breathe deeply: The involuntary mechanism that regulates the swapping of chemicals between our blood and the atmosphere is triggered by a series of very complex neurological responses to internal and external stimuli. The central controls for respiration are in the brain, so changing the way we think about breathing is more effective than forcing the rib cage to expand.

—Veronique Vienne
The Art of Doing Nothing

Pain-Coping Practice Builds a Pain-Coping Mindset

Cornerstone **to building** **a pain-coping** **mindset:** **Practice** **frequently** **in your** **ordinary life.**

I will practice being aware while engaged in (choose a non-stressful daily activity):

____

____

It's not hard to practice these "techniques" in a quiet room. The real challenge is to be able to continue practicing in the midst of emotional stress (i.e., traffic jams, being late, an argument) or physical discomfort (headache, hunger, backache,etc.). Every day, practice one "technique" during stress; notice how it brings you into the moment, into quiet mind and breath awareness.

When pain-coping "techniques" become a "habit" they work better in stressful situations like labor. Habits are formed through repetition. Our stressful daily lives, fortunately (or unfortunately) offer hundreds of opportunities to practice mindfulness and to develop the ability to concentrate intensively under stress.

Being in-labor is a continuation of your life; it's not a separate event. Labor, like life, is a continuous series of activities, including waves of emotional and physical stress. So, don't limit your image of coping in labor to just sitting relaxed in a chair or on a beach. Instead, practice in the flow of your everyday ordinary life. Choose one activity you do every day, like preparing food, washing dishes or tending to the garden. Make a commitment to practice one of the following pain-coping "techniques" for at least five minutes every day while engaged in this activity. Notice what happens with your breath, emotions, sensations, and what helps you to stay focused in quiet mind.

The linear structure of language makes quiet mind impossible to describe, but if you want to experience it, here's a hint: In the absence of judging, one is fully present to what is happening on the outside while experiencing the natural state of "quiet mind" within. In this state, one witnesses what is happening in pure awareness, much like the experience of seeing the tapestry of your dreams without judging what's unfolding.

When quiet mind and awareness of breath become a part of your moment- to-moment living, that awareness will just continue almost effortlessly into the first contraction, and the next . . . into pushing . . . into mothering.

Breath Awareness (BA)

There is a way of breathing
that's a shame and a suffocation.
And there's another way of expiring,
a love breath
that lets you open infinitely.
—Rumi

The practice of Breath Awareness is the foundation for building a pain-coping mindset. Breath Awareness differs from typical labor "breathing techniques" in the following ways:

1. Breath Awareness is rooted in a trust that the mother's body will breathe *itself* perfectly during labor, in the same way she assumes it will regulate her heart rate and digestive functions.

2. Breath Awareness is simply this: the mother is aware of her breath moment-to-moment—she is a "witness" to her natural breath pattern without controlling it or following any preconceived patterns of breathing. For this reason, laboring women throughout the world practice breath awareness (without calling it BA), because it is the most natural thing to do.

3. Fiercely concentrating on your outward breath, with wholehearted effort not to bring judgment or a story to mind, brings about the profound state of quiet mind. Suffering is born of "monkey mind," i.e., story-telling and trying to think one's way through or out of labor.

4. Even when you are practicing Breath Awareness "perfectly," you may still feel the ice (or labor pain), but by giving your full attention to the outward breath—you will bring yourself into quiet mind and may not"suffer."

*When you think about it, what is the difference between **pain** and **suffering**?*

Key Instructions

- Bring your full awareness to your breathing.
- Notice exactly when the exhalation begins . . . and ends.
- Make no effort to change your breathing in any way.
- Just notice . . . Is your outward breath long/shallow? Soft/tight?
- If your mind begins to wander, or you feel the ice . . . Don't think!

  Bring your full attention back to your next outward breath and keep going.
- Practice for the length of an average contraction, about 60-seconds.

Try each of the following variations through a 60-second "ice-contraction."
What happens when you practice Breath Awareness while:

- Moving, rocking, or swaying in rhythm with your breath. Are you moving into, with or away from the sensation of the ice?

- Leaning back or slouching in a chair, closing your eyes, and relaxing:

- Listening to music:

- Visualizing: Imagine that your oxygen-rich lungs are a big sponge with a blotting surface equal to that of the space occupied by the pain and, that this surface that can "actually mop up physiological tensions and dissolve them into the atmosphere with each exhalation."

- Focus on and intentionally resist or complain about distractions in the room. (If necessary, create a distraction by putting on a radio, TV commercials, or practice during a hectic, distracting time of the day).
  a) Notice what you told yourself about the distractions and how that mind chatter affected your experience of Breath Awareness or pain.

  b) During this "ice-contraction" don't tell yourself a story about the distractions. Instead, use Breath Awareness to breathe-*in* the distraction . . . exhale-*into* the distraction.

  c) What happens when you become one with the distraction instead of trying to push it away or blame it for your difficulties? Leaning forward in your chair, "leaning into the pain," moving or relaxing as you're called to.

What Fathers and Birth Companions Need to Know

Sometimes in labor, mothers are too exhausted to maintain pain-coping practice on their own. They may find it helpful to be "talked through" a few contractions to get back on track. Some moms like to be talked through contractions *throughout* labor.

In labor, because of high endorphins and exhaustion, mothers naturally become "spacey" as labor progresses. This is helpful in surrendering to labor, but it also means she may not be able to remember or concentrate on a pain-coping practice- and that's where you come in.

Here are a few tips

Watch her: When she is breathing IN, say, "Notice your next breath out," or "As you breathe out, notice what you are hearing."

Don't tell her to "Breathe" or how to breathe, i.e., slowly, or to follow a particular pattern.

Keep any suggested imagery simple. Consider changing your suggestion after six to eight contractions. Practice with the mom through several "ice-contractions." Listen to her feedback and fine-tune your labor support skills—before labor.

date ____________

• • • ____________________

Ovarian Breathing

Years ago I discovered Ovarian Breathing when reading a book about an ancient Chinese practice called the Microcosmic Orbit. I found it simultaneously deeply relaxing and re-energizing in my own life. One day, as a last resort, I taught it to an exhausted and discouraged laboring mother in her 27th hour—and it made a remarkable difference! Since then, we have taught it to hundreds of parents, many of whom swear by it.

Ovarian Breathing will help you:

- *Re-focus and quiet your mind during distracting moments or transitions, such as during admission to a hospital;*
- *Re-energize, especially toward the end of labor;*
- *Share a deeply harmonious, essentially non-verbal, connection with your partner.*

What To Do:

There are two parts to learn; each partner needs to learn both parts.

Part One: The Breathing Circuit

1. First, get the hand of the breathing circuit on your own.

2. Throughout this practice, increase your concentration by keeping your eyes at rest or closed; looking around the room will draw your attention outward or upward into your thinking mind.

3. Imagine pulling your inward breath up from the base of your spine to the crown of your head.

4. During the pause between in-breath and out-breath, hold your attention at the crown of your head.

5. As you breathe out, follow your exhale from the crown of your head down through your body.

6. As you are breathing out, imagine that every organ, every cell in your body, is being renewed and re-energized; imagine your baby bathed in this life-giving energy.

7. Picture a special bowl resting just above your pubic bone, "collecting" and conserving the precious vitality raining down in your outward breath. Collect this force—don't let it "leak" out.

8. Rest in the pause. . . the infinite space between outward and inward breath. Again, as you inhale, focus on drawing your inward breath up; imagine your breath is following the curves along the inside of your spine.

9. During the pause between the inward and outward breath, focus your attention on the crown of your head.

10. Then, follow your outward breath from beginning to end, downward through the body as you imagine it re-energizing every cell in your body, *re-energizing your womb and your baby.*

What Fathers & Birth Companions Need to Know

In labor, because of super abundant endorphins and exhaustion, mothers *naturally* become "spacey" as labor progresses. This is helpful in surrendering to labor, but it also means she may not be able to remember or concentrate on a pain-coping practice.

Follow *her* labor rhythm by breathing with her, while touching her as described below, to non-verbally help her focus on her breath and the imagery of Ovarian Breathing. Here's how to do it (this takes a little practice):

Enhancing Ovarian Breathing with Touch

1. Begin by placing your hand flat (your right hand if you are right-handed), and somewhat firmly, over her sacrum.

2. As she inhales, move your hand upward from her sacrum to the crown of her head, until it rests ln top of her head. The Chinese teach that the hand should rest on the crown with the "weight of a nickel."

3. If she has long hair, avoid getting tangled in it—drape it over one shoulder or move your hand up her back (quickly skipping over her hair if necessary), to the crown of her head.

4. Place your other hand (the left hand if you are right-handed) flat, with reassuring, full contact, over her sternum (heart chakra) or the top of her big round belly. (Don't tickle her with a light fingertip touch. Do not touch, or wave your hand over, her face—this will probably drive her crazy in labor.)

5. In synchrony with her exhalation, draw your hand down over her belly. Your hand will come to rest on her belly above her pubic bone. She may find the suggestion, "breathe into my hand," as she exhales encourages a longer exhalation, and brings her down out of her thinking mind into her body.

6. One hand should always remain in contact with her body, while the other hand moves into position. If at any time both hands are off her body, her concentration will be disrupted.

After practicing this for a few minutes, reverse roles and learn to give or to receive the other half of this practice. Give constructive feedback to your partner so you can master this before labor begins.

If the mother is being monitored during labor, belts may restrict you from freely moving your hands in this way. So, talk her through Ovarian Breathing and rest one hand on her lower belly so her energy and effort is directed toward the work of labor.

Non-Focused Awareness

Read: *Birthing From Within*, pages 216-222

In labor, you experience many sensations–the temperature in the room, the light, scents, sounds of birds singing, music, words being spoken, touch or massage, nausea, exhaustion, thirst, sweating, chills, warm water in a shower or bath, the cold floor. In ignoring these so called "neutral" sensations, parents position them in the "background" allowing pain and exhaustion to dominate the "foreground" of their awareness–which then amplifies the intensity of pain and exhaustion.

PRACTICING NFA WILL HELP YOU:

- *Use distractions in labor to deepen trance and concentration;*
- *Enter into Quiet Mind to overcome any downward spiral of negative thinking;*
- *Shift focus away from the pain or other negative stimuli;*
- *Increases endurance.*

WHAT TO DO

Throughout this practice, bring your full attention to breath and sensations. You may still feel the ice or labor pain. The purpose of NFA is to stop the mental suffering induced by chatter and to stop focusing on the pain. You do not have to "relax" during this practice; feel free to move about. In fact, practicing while you go about your ordinary activity is the best way to master it.

Holding ice, practice 60-second ice-contractions.

- *Begin by **noticing** your first outward breath...*
  Concentrate your mind by keeping your eyes softly focused in a steady, downward gaze...
  Breathe-in the space and everything in it...

- *Notice what you are **seeing**. As you breathe-in, drink with your eyes the colors, shadows and shapes your eyes are resting on. Without "looking" or labeling what you are seeing, as you exhale, breathe-into what you are seeing.*

- *Notice what you are **hearing**. Breathe-in the sounds completely until there is no sound "out there." Without "listening" or labeling the sound, exhale deeply into the sound--in such a way "you" merge into the sound.*

- *Notice what is **touching** you... and what you are touching. Let your attention go to wherever the pain is not. Breathe-in the sensation of touch (e.g., your feet touching the floor, a breeze in your hair). Breathe slowly into the sliver of space between you and what is touching you.*

- *Keep going.. .follow your **breath** and sensations throughout the contraction ...and rest in this awareness during the rest period between contractions, too.*

A Few More Important Points

1. There's not one right way to practice NFA. You can:

   - *Focus on any one of the sensations (seeing, hearing, etc.) throughout a contraction; or*
   - *Intentionally bring your attention to your sensory awareness following a pattern, i.e., notice three things you are seeing, three things you are hearing, etc. This works well for pre-occupying the left-hemisphere so it's not engaged in thinking and judging. Or*
   - *Notice sensations randomly.*

2. Notice if it helps to cope with the pain if you notice faster. . . slower.
3. At the peak of a contraction, it may be most helpful just to notice your outward breaths. . . then, when you are able to begin noticing the sensations in the room again, resume. . .seeing. . . hearing. . . touch.
4. Between contractions, abide in Quiet Mind through the practice of Breath Awareness or NFA.

Practice: Ice-contraction & Variations

date ____________

. . . ____________

Seeing

Hearing

Touch

Breath

Finding The Center

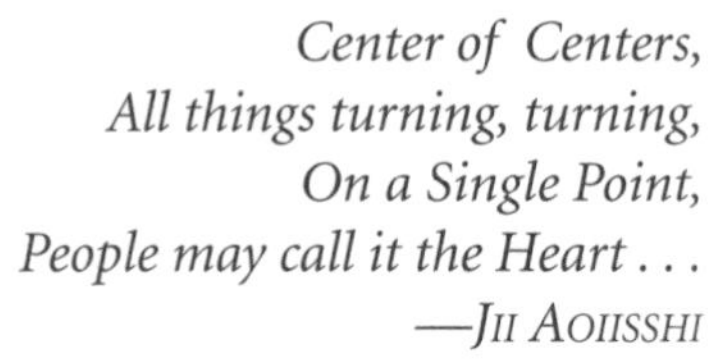

Center of Centers,
All things turning, turning,
On a Single Point,
People may call it the Heart . . .
—JII AOIISSHI

Bring your full attention to your outward breath . . .
As you breathe into the sensation . . .
Find its center . . .
With each breath out, notice how both the center . . .
and the sensation . . .
are in constant movement.
Focus your mind's eye on the center . . .

Write about what happened for you during this process.

date ____________________

. . . ____

Experiment & Practice

What happens when you add imagery? Practicing the following visualizations will steady your mind and strengthen your resolve—especially in active labor.

1. Being in the Eye of a Hurricane

It's far more dangerous to be in the periphery of a hurricane's raging wind than in its calm center where pilots fly safely for many hours. This metaphor guides the laboring woman coping with an emotional or physical storm of labor. Imagine sensation and distractions as the periphery of the hurricane.

2. Going Through the Pain

With each outward breath drive your mind's eye into the center of the sensation—and experience the stillness. Even when you feel the sensation, take courage and with your mind's eye, find the center again, and exhale long and strong into it and see what happens:

A father in one of my classes made this connection between *Going Through the Pain* and martial arts: when a martial artist intends to break a board with a strike of her hand, she doesn't envision striking the board—she envisions moving her hand through the board.

Instead of breathing *at* the sensation, breathe *into* the center of it, or breathe *through* to the "other side."

Using ice, approach this exercise in two ways and notice the difference.

- *First, create an ambivalent internal mindset, in which doubt and an intention to avoid pain cause your breath to "bounce off" the sensation.*
- *Approach the second "ice-contraction" with an unwavering commitment to go through the sensation without the slightest doubt or hesitation.*

Releasing the Natural Sounds of Labor

Read: *Birthing From Within,* pages 227-239

In classic Greek drama there is a chorus composed of actors whose role it is to express latent fears in tragic scenes. The chorus intuitively hears and speaks for the land and the people. With their groans, the chorus encourages spectators to experience what Aristotle referred to as catharsis–that healing sense of renewal that comes from releasing tensions.

This experience echoes the vocalization made during lovemaking and in labor; there is a primal connection between the noises, breathlessness, and moaning. Birth companions often make labor sounds with the mother. Instead of feeling watched, the mother shares an incredible moment when their two voices become one.

date ________________

. . .

The Mindful Use of Narcotics or Other Drugs in Labor

Read: *Birthing From Within,* pages 244-245, 252-253

Part of holistic preparation includes mentally preparing for circumstances where using Pitocin or narcotic-type drugs would be exercising wisdom, not weakness. Get information from your birth attendant or mentor before labor. List situations where drugs would be supportive, rather than routine or disruptive in labor.

- *Find out which drugs are commonly used in labor, or routinely prescribed by your doctor (or hospital).*
- *Find out what's within your power to unfold labor naturally.*
- *What questions will you ask to determine if a drug (or induction) is the best or only solution?*

Did You Know?

• Induction is medically required in only 3 percent of pregnancies.
—Dr. Caldreyo-Barcia

• 81% of women in US hospitals receive Pitocin either to induce or augment their labors.
—Robbie Davis-Floyd, *Cultural Anthropologist at the University of Texas*

• Between 40 and 50 percent of inductions "fail."
—Mothering Magazine, *March-April 2001*

PROTECT YOUR UNBORN BABY

"Labor should be induced only when medically necessary, never simply for convenience or because [you] are sick of being pregnant. The risks in these situations far outweigh the perceived benefits . . . We are just beginning to understand the long-term effects on the fetal brain of drugs such as Pitocin, and the exact long-term effects of inducing or augmenting labor are unknown."

"Not all babies appear to be harmed by the inducing or augmenting of labor, but these procedures do carry risks. According to Doris Haire, 'The fact that Pitocin can shorten the normal oxygenating intervals that occur between contractions is a threat to the integrity of the fetal brain and can have lifelong consequences for the affected baby.'"

"Babies born from natural, spontaneous labors have the best overall outcomes."

"Pitocin has never been approved by the FDA for the use of augmenting labor."

—Mothering Magazine, *March-April 2001*

date ________________

• • • ________________

What I Need to Find Out To Birth-in-Awareness With An Epidural

Read: ***Birthing From Within,*** **pages 240-252**

Write freely

What I feel about any of the following

Labors that call for drugs and epidurals:

How I'll know if I need drugs or an epidural in labor:

The saying "An epidural doesn't have to stop you from birthing from within."

Answers I Need to Pursue Through My Questions

This Symbol is a Reminder to Birth-in-Awareness

Birth Art Assignment

Envision birthing-in-awareness, even if drugs
or epidurals are part of your birth.
Let images and words surface and form a
symbol that will remind you in labor.

Write what came up for when you drew this picture, or when you look at it now.
Refer to Appendix A for more questions that will help you learn from your birth art.

date ______________

. . . ______________________________

Symbol of Birthing-In-Awareness

My New Image of Labor Pain

Do this exercise *after* you've learned the BFW pain-coping techniques, and without looking back at your first sketch of *Labor Pain.*

BIRTH ART ASSIGNMENT

Take just a minute to draw your strongest image of labor pain, or coping with pain, in one of the frames. Be honest. Draw whatever first comes to mind. (Use pastels or markers.)

Compare what you are feeling and envisioning now with how you felt before you started to build your pain-coping mindset, then journal.

date __________

• • •

My Evolving Image of Labor Pain

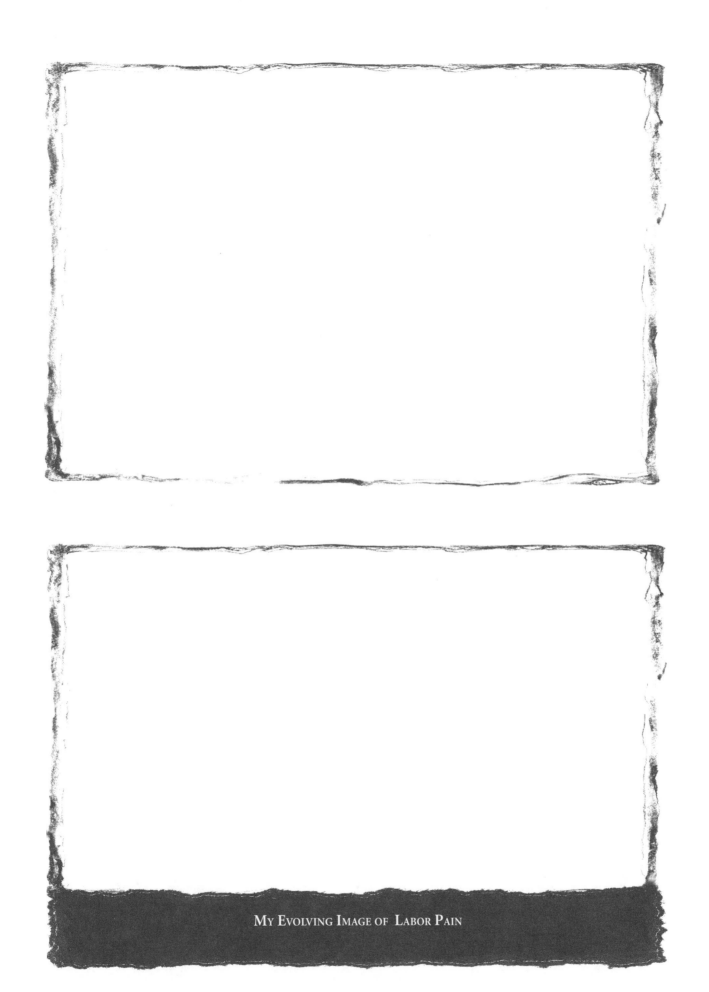

Notes & Personal Reflections

date ________________

. . . ____________________

SECTION • EIGHT

A Gentle & Mindful Transition To Parenthood

when your baby is born so are you as parents "born"

Postpartum Expectations: Hers

After your baby comes, everything changes. There's more to do, and less time to do it. The easiest time to begin sorting out what needs to be done and who's gonna do it before your baby comes. Use this exercise to check your expectations and begin a constructive dialogue. Fill out the questionnaire on your own, then compare your answers.

Suggested Reading:
When Partners Become Parents
by Philip and Carolyn Cowan.

While the baby needs to be cared for, who will usually do the following?

___**Cook Meals**

Clean Up After the Meals

___Wash the dishes or start the dishwasher
___Put the dishes away
___Clean the kitchen: put away the food, clean sink, wipe down counters and stove, sweep and mop the floor, and take out the trash
___Shop for groceries and put the groceries away

Laundry
Did you know that for each load of laundry you do now, you will do four loads after your baby comes?

___Wash the laundry, and about how often?
___Dry the laundry
___Fold or hang the laundry and put it away

Daily "Tidy-Up" of the House

___Clean the diaper pail (if you have one)
___Pick up newspapers, magazines, clothes, and such
___Vacuum and dust
___Clean the bathroom, which means someone must get to it before the black mold starts climbing up the tiles or little things start crawling on the sink, Windex the toothpaste spray off the mirror, scrub the tub and the toilet, change the empty toilet paper roll, and empty the garbage pail

___**Feed the Pets**

___**Pay the Bills**

___**Put in a New Light Bulb When the Old One Burns Out**

___**Take the Baby to the Doctor for Well-Baby Visits**

___**Arrange Child-Care for Your "Dates"**

In the Cowans' comprehensive study of the challenges 72 couples faced from mid-pregnancy to the children's kindergarten years, they found that the greater the discrepancy between a wife's expectation of her husband's involvement and his actual involvement, the more her satisfaction in the marriage declined in the first 18 months after birth.

busy available withdrawn loving helpful…

Grandparents could be emotionally supportive; financially or materially supportive; intrusive, respectful . . .

This is a sentence-completion exercise; write down your first thought.

During the early postpartum transition:

I think that becoming a mother will make me feel more: ____________________
I think becoming a father will make him feel more: ____________________

Becoming parents will change our relationship, and I imagine he will be more ____________________
____________________ toward me/us.
I think I will be ____________________ toward him.

I am most concerned about: ____________________
I think my partner is most concerned about: ____________________

I'm envisioning childcare will be shared in this way: ____________________
____

I think my partner envisions sharing childcare in this way: ____________________
____

When my parents become grandparents, I expect them to be: ____________________
When his parents become grandparents I think they will be: ____________________

When we become parents, my relationships with my/his parents will: ____________________
When we become parents, I think my partner's relationships with my/his parents will: ____________________

Our friends and social life will: ____________________
I imagine my partner thinks our friends and social life will: ____________________

During the time-consuming first year of our baby's life I know I'll have to make sacrifices. What I will miss the most is: ____________________
I think my partner will miss: ____________________

I think that the father's role in the breastfeeding relationship is: ____________________
I think my partner views his role as: ____________________

Postpartum Expectations: His

After your baby comes, everything changes. There's more to do, and less time to do it. The easiest time to begin sorting out what needs to be done and who's gonna do it before your baby comes. Use this exercise to check your expectations and begin a constructive dialogue. Fill out the questionnaire on your own, then compare your answers.

Suggested Reading:
When Partners Become Parents
by Philip and Carolyn Cowan.

While the baby needs to be cared for, who will usually do the following?

___**Cook Meals**

Clean Up After the Meals

___Wash the dishes or start the dishwasher
___Put the dishes away
___Clean the kitchen: put away the food, clean sink, wipe down counters and stove, sweep and mop the floor, and take out the trash
___Shop for groceries and put the groceries away

Laundry
Did you know that for each load of laundry you do now, you will do four loads after your baby comes?

___Wash the laundry, and about how often?
___Dry the laundry
___Fold or hang the laundry and put it away

Daily "Tidy-Up" of the House

___Clean the diaper pail (if you have one)
___Pick up newspapers, magazines, clothes, and such
___Vacuum and dust
___Clean the bathroom, which means someone must get to it before the black mold starts climbing up the tiles or little things start crawling on the sink, Windex the toothpaste spray off the mirror, scrub the tub and the toilet, change the empty toilet paper roll, and empty the garbage pail

___**Feed the Pets**

___**Pay the Bills**

___**Put in a New Light Bulb When the Old One Burns Out**

___**Take the Baby to the Doctor for Well-Baby Visits**

___**Arrange Child-Care for Your "Dates"**

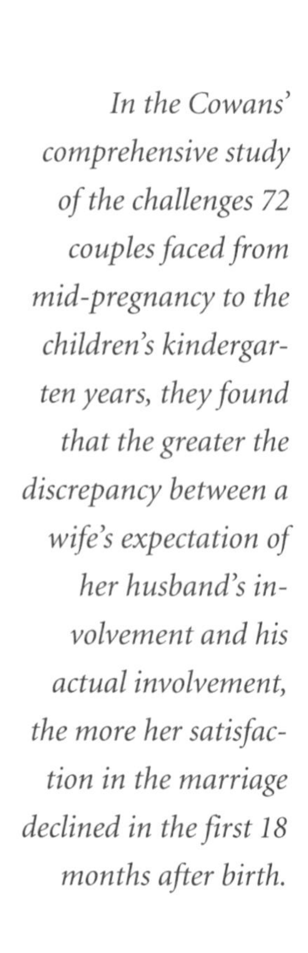

In the Cowans' comprehensive study of the challenges 72 couples faced from mid-pregnancy to the children's kindergarten years, they found that the greater the discrepancy between a wife's expectation of her husband's involvement and his actual involvement, the more her satisfaction in the marriage declined in the first 18 months after birth.

busy available withdrawn loving helpful . . .

Grandparents could be emotionally supportive; financially or materially supportive; intrusive, respectful . . .

This is a sentence-completion exercise; write down your first thought.

During the early postpartum transition:

I think that becoming a father will make me feel more: ____________________________________

I think becoming a mother will make her feel more: ____________________________________

Becoming parents will change our relationship, and I imagine she will be more ______________________________ toward me/us.

I think I will be ______________________________ toward her.

I am most concerned about: ____________________________________

I think my partner is most concerned about: ____________________________________

I'm envisioning childcare will be shared in this way: ____________________________________

____

I think my partner envisions sharing childcare in this way: ____________________________________

____

When my parents become grandparents, I expect them to be: ____________________________________

When her parents become grandparents I think they will be: ____________________________________

When we become parents, my relationships with my/her parents will: ______________________________

When we become parents, I think my partner's relationships with my/her parents will: __________________

Our friends and social life will: ____________________________________

I imagine my partner thinks our friends and social life will: ____________________________________

During the time-consuming first year of our baby's life I know I'll have to make sacrifices. What I will miss the most is: ____________________________________

I think my partner will miss: ____________________________________

I think that my role in the breastfeeding relationship is: ____________________________________

I think my partner views my role as: ____________________________________

How closely did your expectations match?

date __________

. . .

The [Cowan] study also found that when fathers were strongly involved in caring for their 6-month old infants, it paid huge dividends: their own self-esteem and their wives' satisfaction with marriage all tended to go up during the first 18 months. What's more, couples with involved fathers reported less parenting stress.

—Larry Letich
Family Networker

date ____________

. . . ____________

Our Postpartum Transition Plan Worksheets

Read: ***Birthing From Within,*** **pages 260-264**

Write down every person who could be a support to you and their phone number–your friends and family, co-workers, neighbors, church or organization pals, your mentor, midwife, doula–anyone. When you are in need of a friendly voice or advice, but too tired or overwhelmed to find a phone number, the numbers will be handy and easy to call.

My List of Phone Friends

Names	**Phone Numbers / Email**

"She is a friend of me.
She gather me, man.
The pieces I am, she
gather them and give
them back to me in
all the right order.
It's good, you know,
when you got a
woman who is a
friend of your mind."

—Tony Morrison
Beloved

Oprah, August 29, 2001

Instructions for making your Postpartum Transition Plan Worksheet:
Fold a large sheet of paper into quarters. Get out your magic markers. Label the sheet and each quadrant like the example on the following page. Fill out each section according to the directions that follow, then hang it on your refrigerator or in a place you can easily read it later.

Our Postpartum Transition Plan

PHONE FRIENDS

(SEE PREVIOUS PAGE)

NAME	PHONE / EMAIL

POSTPARTUM MEAL ANGELS

(SEE PAGE 186)

CAPTAIN

Before my baby's first birthday, I will
FOLLOW MY BLISS
by doing each thing listed at least once, and by supporting my partner to do the same.

(SEE NEXT TWO PAGES)

Mother's	*Date I followed my Bliss*
Father's	*Date I followed my Bliss*
Our Bliss List as a couple	*Date I followed my Bliss*

OUR TOP FIVE TRANSITION CONCERNS & A STRATEGY

(SEE PAGE 187)

Follow Your Bliss

If you follow your bliss, you put yourself on a kind of track
that has been there all the while, waiting for you,
and the life that you ought to be living is the one you are living. . .
I say follow your bliss and don't be afraid, and doors will open
where you didn't know they were going to be . . .
Wherever you are—if you are following your bliss,
you are enjoying that refreshment,
that life within you, all the time . . ."

– Joseph Campbell

Too many parents at the end of their baby's first year, or even eighteen years later, realize that they gave up the things they loved to do and that gave them bliss when they became parents. Becoming a conscious parent does require sacrifice, and it also requires modeling for our children how to live creative, balanced lives.

Living my bliss as a parent

Write three things that have brought you bliss in the past. Maybe you are doing it now or perhaps it's something you've always wanted to do but never made happen. Keep in mind that you will be fulfilling your Bliss List as a new parent, so white-water rafting trips or skiing the Alps may not be realistic at this time.

Mom

Dad/Partner

How can we bring bliss to our relationship?

By living our bliss as a way of life.

Bill Moyers asked Joseph Campbell, "What happens when you follow your bliss?" and Campbell answered, "You come to bliss. In the Middle Ages, a favorite image that occurs in many, many contexts is the wheel of fortune. There's the hub of the wheel, and there is the revolving rim of the wheel. For example, if you are attached to the rim of the wheel of fortune, you will be either above going down or at the bottom coming up. But if you are at the hub, you are in the same place all the time. That is the sense of the marriage vow I take you in health or sickness, in wealth or poverty: going up or going down. But I take you as my center, and you are my bliss, not the wealth that you might bring me, not the social prestige, but you. That is following your bliss."

Jot down two or three things that lead you as a couple to Bliss. It could be something you are doing now, that you used to do but have lost track of, or even something you've always wanted to do together but haven't made happen yet.

Living our bliss...

date ____________

• • • ____

Postpartum Meal Angels

Read: ***Birthing From Within,*** **pages 266-267**

Ask a friend who has a talent for organizing to be your "Meal Angel Captain" and to arrange your postpartum meals-on-wheels before your baby is born. Some parents have friends and family fill out a meal-calendar at their Mother Blessing or Baby Shower.

Sunday	Monday	Tuesday	Wednesday	Thursday	Friday	Saturday

List potential meal angels.

1 ______________________________

2 ______________________________

3 ______________________________

4 ______________________________

5 ______________________________

6 ______________________________

7 ______________________________

OUR DIVISION OF HOUSEHOLD CHORES

Read: ***Birthing From Within*, page 263**

List anticipated stressors and brainstorm strategies and solutions.

1 ______

2 ______

3 ______

4 ______

5 ______

6 ______

7 ______

Did you know that most couples name division of household chores as their number one postpartum stress?

A small survey was conducted in a Constructive Living, "Renewing Your Relationship" program. Participating couples were asked what they argued most frequently about. The leading answer was "children," the second answer was "disorganized living space." Clearly the "stuff" of our lives has the potential to wreak havoc not only with our own minds and lives, but with others who must share the same space with us."

—CONSTRUCTIVE LIVING QUARTERLY, FALL 2000

I remember reading a story on the internet about a father who came home from work one night to find his children playing in the yard in their pajamas, piles of dirty laundry in the bathroom, clean unfolded laundry on the couch in the livingroom, dirty dishes in the sink, bowls of spilled cereal on the table in the family room, toys littering the floor of the hallway, the TV on, and dinner still in the freezer. His wife was in bed reading her Good Housekeeping magazine, eating bon bons. When he asked, "What happened here?" she answered, "You know how you ask me what I do all day? Well, today I didn't do it - now, you know!"

— TOLD TO ME BY CHANTAL DESOTO,
Hypnotherapist and Certified BFW Mentor,
Santa Cruz, California

Postpartum Healing & Body Care

Read: ***Birthing From Within,*** **pages 267-272**

Jot down questions or good advice as you learn from women experienced in birth, childbirth class, or reading.

date ____________

. . . ____________

Nourishing, Soothing Postpartum Baths

Read: ***Birthing From Within,*** **pages 269-270**

AFTER-BIRTH SITZ BATHS

Even if your perineum is intact after birth, your bottom may be a little sore the first few days or weeks after giving birth. Taking soothing herbal baths will speed up the healing process. Many herbal stores sell Sitz Bath as a pre-mixed combination of dried herbs, or you can make up your own. You can find a recipe for herbal sitz bath in *BFW*.

ANYTIME—AFTER YOUR PERINEUM HAS HEALED

Create a little ambience.

Light a candle or incense and play soothing music.

Scent the bath water with floral salts, aroma-therapy, or a few drops of ginger or balsam oil.

Float rose and flower petals in the water.

Creamy Milk Bath

1 cup cornstarch
2 cups dry milk powder
1/8 teaspoon scented oil,
vanilla or almond.
Blend the dry ingredients, mix with a little hot bath water as you're filling the tub.

Strawberries & Cream Summertime Bath

Add to running hot bath water:
1 cup powdered milk
1/2 cup oatmeal
A teaspoon of strawberry essential oil
After your bath wrap up in a dry, warm towel.
Lie down, listen to music, get a foot massage, and have a light snack.

RECIPE FOR A GOURMET NAP

The long afternoon nap (with your baby) is for sleep connoisseurs— it's an after-dessert delicacy. To make sure you wake up refreshed, follow these easy steps.

- *If you don't have shutters, draw the blinds or the curtains. The room should be bathed in a soft, restful glow.*
- *Kick off your shoes. Only remove garments that are constricting or that would rumple badly. You want to be somewhat dressed up for the occasion: The gourmet nap is a formal affair.*
- *Glance at the clock, take off your watch, and decide when you want to wake up. Trust your subconscious to nudge you when your time is up (if the baby doesn't do it first).*
- *Lie down under the covers but not between the sheets. Close your eyes and imagine that you are in a small boat, about to embark on a short journey. Pull up the anchor and let the boat drift. The water may feel choppy at first, but soon the waves will diminish and you'll be sailing on a smooth sea. You'll be awakened by a bump—your keel is scraping a sandy bottom. Drag yourself out of bed slowly, as if you were pulling your skiff onto a beach.*
- *Throw water on your face, stretch, open the window. Don't rush. You've got plenty of time ahead of you.*

—VERONIQUE VIENNE
The Art of Doing Nothing

Postpartum Exercises

Not until after my third child was born did I come to grips with the fact that my body would never be the same, and that I would never be the same. I was then able to accept my new mother-body and nurture it . . . and understood that I could not and should not compare it to how it was before I became a mother.
—Marie, mother of three

TO LEARN A COMPLETE SERIES OF POSTPARTUM EXERCISES, read *A Complete Guide for Postpartum Women* by ROBIN LIM, *Chapters 8 and 9*

Suzanne Palmer, a mother and mentor in Albuquerque, designed these unique postpartum exercises for mothers' body, mind and spirit: Gently lay down on the floor with your back flat, your knees up, and feet firmly planted hip-width apart. You can place a comfortable pillow under your head if you like.

Place your hands on your belly, lovingly stroke lazy circles around your soft belly—and acknowledge the life you created within your body, and how your body yielded, stretched and surrendered . . . month after month—opening to release your baby into your waiting arms.

And genuinely claim, even shout, three times,

I am an Amazing Woman and my Body did a Magnificent Thing.

I am an Amazing Woman and my Body did a Magnificent Thing.

I AM AN AMAZING WOMAN AND MY BODY DID AN AMAZING THING.

Make a sketch of your Amazing Mother Body.

Write your own affirmation. Write about how you are cultivating a loving respect for the new mother-body you have right now.

ABDOMINAL EXERCISES

date ____________

. . . ____

____

____

____

____

____

____

Grow Baby, Grow!

Weight gain patterns

Expect your baby to lose weight during his or her first week of life—at least 5-7%, up to 10%—it happens all the time because it's NORMAL; it's due to the shedding of excess fluids present in the baby's tissues at birth and the passage of meconium (baby's first bowel movements).

With regular feeding (breast or bottle), your baby should steadily regain its birth weight within two to three weeks of age. The more weight a baby loses, the longer it may take to regain it; so, long as your baby is gaining about 0.9 ounces a day, be patient. If you are breastfeeding, giving your baby water or formula to resolve this normal pattern may actually slow his or her weight gain, and could cause nipple confusion.

Other signs baby is getting enough milk

There'll be one or two wet diapers a day in the first three to four days. After 3-4 days, there should be six wet diapers and two bowel movements each day. After six weeks, some breastfed babies have fewer bowel movements; once every four to ten days is normal.

Two reasons why a baby wouldn't gain weight

1. Foremilk-Hindmilk Imbalance: If your baby is not gaining weight, and its stools are green and watery, it could be a sign that you are not letting your baby nurse long enough to "empty the breast" or feedings are too short and at too frequent intervals (i.e., every hour) causing a foremilk/hindmilk imbalance. ***Foremilk***, rich in water soluble vitamins and lactose, but low in fat is equivalent to skim milk. Lactose stimulates the baby's digestive tract to move the milk through quickly. ***Mid-milk***, released after 5-8 minutes of nursing, is the "whole milk." ***Hindmilk***, the milk that comes towards the end of a 15-minute feeding, is high-calorie fat-rich milk "Haagen-Dazs milk." Hindmilk comprises only 5% of a feeding's volume, but it's the milk that plumps up your baby.

2. Mother's Diet is Deficient in Calories or Fluid Intake: It is recommended a nursing mother consume 2700-3000 calories a day, although some moms and babies get by with less. If your baby is fussy after feedings and isn't gaining enough weight, check your diet, and add calories and protein to your diet (i.e., a glass of milk with each nursing)—and see if the volume of milk increases. By two weeks, you'll be making 24-32 ounces of milk a day; your milk averages 20 calories per ounce—if you're volume deficient, your baby gets less calories.

Average weight gain pattern during the first year

Months	Weekly Weight Gain
1-4 months	4-8 oz.
4-6 months	3-5 oz.
6-12 months	1-3 oz.

Look How You've Grown!

Whenever the spirit moves you, record your baby's weight.

Date	Baby's Age	Weight	Length

"I love my little girl an extraordinary amount; I have, in fact, surprised myself with my talent for fathering. Since her birth I have been so wholly preoccupied with the minutiae of her progress— from the growth of the microscopic hairs on her bald head to the lengthening of her attention span—that I have been effectively lost to the larger world."

—Harry Stein
My Daughter, My Joy

Am I Eating Enough?

If you're wondering, or just curious, jot down everything you've eaten during the past 24-hours, including snacks and drinks. It may help to begin with the most recent meal, and work your way backwards.

Date	Breakfast	Lunch	Dinner	Snacks

MILK

What's For Dinner, Mom?

Breastfeeding Diet

Type of Diet	Omnivore	Herbivore	Vegan May need to supplement with Calcium and Vitamin B1
Dairy *1 c. whole milk,buttermilk, yogurt, sour cream* *1/3 c. powdered milk* *1 1/4 c. cottage cheese*	*4 servings*	*4 servings*	*4 choices from alternatives*
Eggs	*2 eggs*	*2 servings*	*none*
Protein from meat, poultry *2 oz. chicken, beef, poultry veal, liver, kidney,* *1/2 c. canned tuna, salmon, mackerel* *6 sardines*	*4 2-oz. servings*	*none*	*none*
Protein from vegetarian sources	*As desired (may substitute for meat servings)*	*3 servings*	*6 servings*
Grains *1 slice yeasted whole-grain bread; 1 corn tortilla; 1/2 roll, bagel or muffin; 1 wholegrain waffle or pancake; 1/2 c. hot cereal, granola; 1/2 c. macaroni, noodles* *1/2 c. cooked rice, millet, bulgur*	*5 servings*	*5 servings*	*5 slices yeasted bread* *4 other choices*
Dark Green Veggies	*2 servings*	*2 servings*	*3 servings*
Fruits and Veggies	*2 servings*	*2 servings*	*3 servings*
Fats	*3 servings*	*3 servings*	*4 servings*

Protein-Calcium Drink

2 Tbsp powdered milk (whole, non-instant)
2 Tbsp peanut butter
2 Tbsp blackstrap molasses
1 Tbsp powdered carob
1 egg
1 tray ice cubes (if you're using a food processor) or
1/2 tray ice cubes and 1 cup water or milk (if you're using a blender)

Put all ingredients together and blend until creamy.
For more calcium and protein you can freeze milk in the ice trays.
Makes two cups.

*One cup of this drink will provide the following nutrients:
Calcium 233 mgs.; Calories 212; Protein 8.3 grams*

Nutritious Postpartum Nurture Bars

submitted by Abby Bordner, BFW Doula, Santa Fe, New Mexico

2 cups rolled oats
1 1/2 cups whole wheat flour
1 cup apple juice
1/4 cup wheat germ or millet flakes
1 cup dried cranberries or other dried fruit
3/4 tsp. cinnamon (plus extra for the top)
4 Tbsp. brown sugar (more or less, depending on your taste)
2 Tbsp. blackstrap molasses
1/2 cup vegetable oil
1/4 cup sesame seed and/or chopped nuts

1. Notice your next outward breath and continue in Breath Awareness as your hands prepare this healthy snack.
2. Preheat over to 375 degrees. Grease 9x13" baking pan.
3. Do 10 kegels.
4. Combine all ingredients and mix well.
5. Touch your belly and say, "I made life here and I gave birth. I am an amazing woman."
6. Transfer ingredients to prepared pan and distribute as evenly as possible, patting the batter in place with your hands. Sprinkle a little extra cinnamon on top.
7. Do 10 more kegels.
8. Bake for 30 minutes.

I made life here and I gave birth. I am an amazing woman.

These Are a Few of My Favorite Things I Want to Remember About Feeding You . . .

Introducing the Back-Up Bottle with Compassion

Read: *Birthing From Within,* pages 273-275

You have probably heard that "Breast is Best." You might want to consider however that even the most dedicated breastfeeding family sometimes benefits from the compassionate use of the back-up bottle. A back-up bottle is not a substitute for the primary breastfeeding relationship and it is not supplementing breastfeeding—it simply increases the baby's feeding flexibility.

Possible benefits of a baby's back-up bottle

There are circumstances in which committed breastfeeding parents have found using the back-up bottle beneficial, such as when a mother:

- *Returns to work, even part-time*
- *Is exhausted and getting four to five hours of uninterrupted sleep would make her feel "sane" again*
- *Becomes sick or needs surgery (during which time the milk supply may diminish and the baby would appreciate a little extra)*
- *Is going on a "date" or taking a little time to "Follow Her Bliss"*
- *Has trouble establishing breastfeeding*

Or if the baby:

- *Has trouble establishing breastfeeding*
- *Becomes ill, needs surgery, or has special needs*
- *Has severe negative (allergic) reactions to the mother's diet or breastmilk*

Circumstances like these do not necessarily warrant back-up bottle feeding:

- *Inverted nipples*
- *Jaundice*
- *Sleepy newborn*
- *Garden variety illnesses, like colds and fevers*
- *Colic, fussy baby or teething*

How To Introduce The Back-Up Bottle Without Interrupting Breastfeeding

1. Start between three and four weeks. Parents who wait until six weeks usually find their baby is "already set in its ways," and will not show any interest in the bottle.

2. Use an Avent nipple (see page 200).

3. At first, a breastfeeding baby often takes a bottle better from someone other than its own beloved breastfeeding mother. If your baby sees and hears you (its breastfeeding mom) in the room whilelearning to take the bottle, he/she may twist and turn in your direction and lose interest in trying the bottle. As a breastfeeding mom, you need (and deserve) little breaks. During back-up bottle "training," refresh yourself with a bath, take a walk, or run an errand; know that others will find joy in spending a little time loving your baby.

4. Offer your baby the back-up bottle once daily for several weeks, or your baby (with its short-term memory) will forget it ever took a bottle.

5. The best time of day is in the evening when you tend to make less milk and baby might like a little extra milk. It's easiest for baby to learn to take the bottle when he/she's not starving. The first few times, offer the bottle after your baby has had a "snack" from mother's breast, or about an hour and a half after an evening feeding when baby is relaxed, awake, hungry but not starving and crying.

6. Be patient. Some babies accept the bottle readily the first time, and continue to move easily back and forth between breast and bottle. Other babies are inconsistent, and need regular "practice" over a week or two before they'll take it consistently.

7. Wrap the baby in some of the mother's clothing; some babies are more relaxed when they can smell their mother's scent while taking the bottle.

8. For many babies breastmilk from the refrigerator is fine, or it can be warmed. Thaw frozen breastmilk under warm tap water. If you use formula, follow product directions.

9. Before you begin feeding, invert the bottle upside down—milk should drip freely from the nipple; warm, flowing milk like mother's. If the nipple is clogged, the baby will not be encouraged or happy.

10. While bottle feeding, cradle the baby in your arms in an "upright" position (versus bottle feeding them while they lie on their backs); this not only prevents "flooding" the baby, but prevents ear infections, too. Try different positions. Some babies prefer being held out on the lap when they take a bottle.

Don't put guilt in your baby's back-up bottle (or in any other baby's bottle)

How much milk should you put in the bottle?

Since back-up bottle feeding is not intended to "supplement" the breast, volume is not as important as opportunity for a baby to learn how to take a bottle. Many parents find an ounce or two is plenty.

Avent Bottles

Not all baby bottles and nipples are the same —Why Avent nipples are best

• The natural broad, long, and soft design of the Avent nipple requires the baby to use its tongue and lips in much the same way it does during breastfeeding.

• During breastfeeding, the baby latches on to the breast with a wide-open mouth covering both the nipple and about one to one-and-a-half inches of the areola. The design of the Avent nipple is long and more closely resembles the natural shape of the mother's nipple while breastfeeding. It's length and shape allow for the correct positioning of the tip of the nipple on the soft palate which is far back in the baby's mouth, which in turn elicits the natural swallowing process.

• Other bottle nipples are shorter and do not reach this area of the baby's mouth, so the baby uses only his or her lips on the tip of the nipple—and this leads to nipple confusion.

• Since the baby uses the same sucking motion on the Avent bottle as on the breast, the transition between bottle and breast is easy for the baby; there is much less risk of nipple confusion.

• Avent is the only nipple featuring an anti-vacuum skirt with a one-way air valve, which eliminates the vacuum that can build up as a baby drinks. When a vacuum forms the nipple collapses, constricting milk flow. Unable to receive milk, a frustrated baby's natural reaction is to suck more vigorously which in turn increases the amount of air swallowed. The Avent nipple's one-way air valve opens and closes with baby's natural sucking rhythm letting air flow into the bottle while baby drinks, preventing a vacuum. Less air in the tummy means fewer incidents of post-feeding discomfort related to colic. You know the nipple's valve is working to prevent a vacuum and reduce air in baby's tummy when you see bubbles in the bottle.

• Avent bottles are available in many stores. For more information visit the Avent website: www.aventamerica.com/aventbottle/

Sucking on an Avent bottle requires baby to open its mouth wide, suck and swallow as it does on the breast, pictured. ***A typical bottle limits sucking motion to the lips.***

My Mommy and Daddy's First Parent-Report Card

You probably have much higher expectations and are harder on yourself as a new parent than your baby. Just for fun, pretend that your baby could read this report card and grade you using a rating scale of "0" as the lowest possible "It ain't happenin' " score; 4-ish for "good enough"— and "7" for achieving "excellence."

Today's date: ________________________

BABY CARE BASICS	MOMMY	DADDY
Feeds me *(Dad gets full points for supporting breastfeeding)* **Diapers me** **Soothes me**		
BABY TALK LANGUAGE ARTS **Learned to interpret my cries** **Talks, coos, and sings to me**		
HOME ECONOMICS **Fulfills share of agreed upon household chores** **Helps with grocery shopping & cooking** **Responds realistically to changes in finances** **My parents help each other without needing to be begged**		
CO-PARENTING SOCIAL SKILLS **Play well together (quality and frequency of fun time)** **Helps my other parent "Follow Their Bliss"** **Tries to understand my other parent's point of view**		
RELATING TO MY GRANDPARENTS **Open to accepting good advice and assistance** **Able to set necessary boundaries** **Allows my grandparents to do their job, i.e., spoil me**		
TOTALS		

PARENT-REPORT CARD GRADING SCALE

0-30 Do you need more help or are your standards too high?

31-60 Good enough *is* good enough!

61-85 Keep up the good work!

85-105 But are you having any fun?

Jot down what surprised you, and any new solution focused strategies.

date ____________________

• • • ____

Birth Stories Workshop

Parents wanting to transform negative feelings related to their births can attend a BFW Birth Story Workshop, make an appointment with a therapist or transform their negative self-beliefs by following the exercise below.

Even when a birth attendant summarizes labor as "uneventful" (meaning reasonably normal), you might have difficulty accepting or resolving a particular moment lived in labor especially if your baby is healthy. Perhaps it is a decision you made or deferred, an interaction, or your own emotional or physical feelings in labor. Sometimes parents discount their experience and bury their feelings when others do not empathize with their grief. If there is a birth memory that keeps coming up, or one that you are trying to forget or minimize, try this exploration process. Bringing images, even "negative" ones, to light through drawing and journaling can be revealing and healing.

Birth Art Assignment

Whenever you think back on your labor, what is the one disappointing or troubling moment that comes to mind? Closing your eyes may help bring it into focus. Imagine you can "replay" an internal video of your labor, birth, or postpartum. As you watch, be aware scene by scene of your feelings, what you are telling yourself, and in particular, notice if there are any "frames" you are avoiding or minimizing. If so, pause, take a good look—open your eyes, grab something to draw with, and draw it on the next page.

Now, before you explore your drawing, let your mind become quiet and receptive.
Look at the drawing you made with beginner's mind and eyes . . . Listen, it will speak to you.
Then, journal your insights .

date ________________

. . . ____

One Disappointing Birth Story

(Birth Story Workshop, continued)

After living through an unexpected, harrowing or humiliating event (even if you managed to cope reasonably well with the situation in the moment), it is common to assume a negative belief about oneself—without even being aware of it—and then, begin to live that belief as if it were true. *This* (not the incident) is the problem!

We live our beliefs whether we are conscious of them or not—and we're rarely conscious of the beliefs that are driving our behavior and emotions. Unchallenged negative beliefs begin to make sense as they insidiously infiltrate our relationships, identity as a parent, and every area of our life.

1. Describe what happened—without defending, complaining, or blaming. Include details about what you were seeing, hearing, feeling, and thinking. Who was involved? Where did it occur?

2. Whenever you think of this moment—(not what you thought at the time it happened), what do you tell yourself it means about you?

3. Get more specific: state your negative self-belief in a short sentence that begins with "I am . . .

4. Sit quietly with this negative belief statement and pay attention to the emotions and images that come up. Become aware of how and where you are carrying this story-image in your body. Feel it. Write about it, sketch it.

Write about the moment /event that inspired your drawing . . .

CROSS THE GREAT RIVER, NO BLAME – I CHING

The profound mystery of birth, including how your birth unfolded as it did, can never be completely understood with the mind. Your mind can come up with theories, but it can never fully explain why anything happens when or as it does.

What happened happened. But if you continue to carry the beliefs you created from it around with you, in a sense it continues to happen *now*. There is a story of two monks walking along in silence. They came upon a river and saw a maiden struggling to cross it. The elder monk wordlessly picked up the maiden, carried her across the river, set her down and continued walking. The younger monk broke his inner silence ruminating about how his companion broke his vows by touching a woman. As the young monk walked along, he became increasingly agitated. Finally, he spoke aloud, challenging the elder brother to account for his actions. The old one responded, "I only carried her across the river, you are still carrying her."

How has "carrying" this negative belief ***about yourself*** *influenced the life you are living, your relationships and your new identity as a parent? Imagine "leaving this negative belief on the bank of the river." Return to your truth, what you know is true about you, and propose a new belief. Below, write a positive, truthful belief that invokes a feeling of well-being and inspires you to live in peace.*

LAY YOUR OLD BELIEF DOWN ON THE RIVER BANK

date ____________

• • • ____

TO HELP YOU REMEMBER YOUR NEW BELIEF OR AFFIRMATION THIS WEEK:

- *Write it and post it in a visible place*
  - *Choose a symbol that represents the belief or feeling, a symbol you will see often or can wear*
    - *Most importantly, hold it in mind continuously as you go about your ordinary day*

During the week, when you think of it, jot down what is different for you emotionally, physically, and in your relationships with others since you've substituted your new positive belief for the old negative one:

WHAT'S HAPPENING?

date ________________

• • • ____

Some Moms Have Postpartum Depression

"My parents' generation would refer to pregnancy as a woman being in a 'delicate condition.' I feel the most delicate condition starts after the baby is born. We need to dispel the motherhood myth and acknowledge that a woman is undergoing a time of incredible biological, emotional and personal change."

—Marie Osmond

Postpartum depression and related illnesses are not well understood, accepted, or tolerated in our society. This Journal would not be complete without addressing the range of psychological changes that occur postpartum, and suggestions to mobilize resources.

When postpartum illness presents, most parents are taken off-guard; they don't know what is happening, what to do, or who to turn to for help. Because the mother may not recognize her own symptoms (or may attempt to repress them if she does), it is important that fathers and other family members or friends are familiar with the symptoms of postpartum depression. There are many approaches to treating postpartum illness. Left untreated, postpartum depression can adversely affect the mother-child relationship, erode a marriage, and worse.

BLUES

Sudden bursts of crying and *fleeting* feelings of sadness, helplessness, hopelessness, and doubts about being a good mother. Blues only last a few days to two weeks after giving birth.

POSTPARTUM DEPRESSION (PPD):

Postpartum depression can be mild to severe; it may begin two to six weeks after giving birth, even as late as three to five months, and lasts six months to a year postpartum. Mothers who develop PPD often have a history of depression or felt depressed during pregnancy, which is unusual because most pregnant mothers feel "euphoric," i.e., a feeling of well-being. Common symptoms can be found on the checklist on the next page.

Could I Have Postpartum Depression?

Take a look at this checklist to familiarize yourself with the symptoms of postpartum depression. Rate the intensity of symptoms: (0) not true at all; (1) slightly true but not interfering with my daily activity; (2) true and is interfering but not keeping me from functioning; (3) very true, unable to function. Keep track of symptoms for 11 days. If you notice that you have mostly 2's and 3's, professional help is recommended.

POSTPARTUM DAY

Symptoms *I am:*											
Crying daily for no real reason, lasting beyond a week											
Feeling anxious, can't sit still											
Feeling profound sadness											
Having panic attacks; racing heart, can't breathe											
Constantly worried about my baby's health or safety											
Not feeling connected to my baby or other people											
Feeling hopeless											
Unmotivated, I'm not taking care of my every day needs											
Afraid of being alone											
Confused											
Unable to concentrate											
Unable to sleep even though I am exhausted											
Exaggerated mood swings: feeling down to feeling too good											
Feeling guilty, unworthy											
Unable to control obsessive thoughts; talking incessantly											
If you have any of the following, seek help immediately: *Suicidal fantasies*											
Fear of or fantasies of harming my baby											
Experiencing bizarre thoughts or dreams											

"Cries for help are usually transmitted "in code." The new mother, who is supposed to be enjoying her baby, has no explanation for what is happening to her. She fears the worst and is ashamed. Confused and frightened, she may seek help through her baby.

—James Alexander Hamilton and Patricia Neel Harberger

Rather than dismiss the following maternal behaviors or attributing them to inexperience or being a little quirky, consider them symptoms of often overlooked and covert signs of postpartum depression:

- *An obsession with counting diapers used each day*
- *Preoccupation with baby's minor symptoms, such as normal sneezing*
- *Frequently calling or visiting the pediatrician or Emergency Room*

THE SILENT CRY FOR HELP

THE SMILING DEPRESSION

It is not uncommon for women who are suffering from postpartum depression to conceal their thoughts behind their determination not to tell anyone. Marie Osmond's candid personal reflections describe what is referred to as smiling depression:"

"I spent five months in the darkest place I've ever been. I'm a woman who had available resources, close friends and family, a present and loving husband and the financial ability to seek out assistance. With access to all this, I still put on the face of being in control. I still insisted to anyone who asked that I was 'fine.'

"Why did I do that? Looking back, I can give two reasons. The first is shame. I couldn't admit to anyone, even my husband, that I was having a hard time coping. How do you express that you are in complete despair when everything you've been told or seen in the media represents new motherhood as the happiest, most fulfilling time in a woman's life? . . . I didn't know anyone else who felt this way.

*"The second reason is immobilization. This is the harshest reality of depression.
I couldn't make a move on my own. Depression robbed me of any energy it would take to make an extra phone call, get an appointment or even try to explain how I felt."*

Marie Osmond
Newsweek, July 2, 2001

One can empathize with a new mother's anxiety and ruminating doubts in the following passage by Judy Katz-Levine:

"The responsibility was too great, so great, she could not tolerate it. She was afraid she couldn't care for her newborn son. Afraid she would drop him on the floor, in the bathtub. She didn't think she could do it. Afraid she would starve him with not enough mother's milk. Fearful of scratching his translucent skin. In sleep he looked like an angel. Like God. He was from God. She was afraid the plane would crash, afraid he'd slip through her fingers. Responsibility like an old hard road. Rutted with cutting stones. She would get lost. Afraid she couldn't. Didn't have the wisdom didn't have the power. Questioning every night, turning like a forgetful tongue. She woke up. Picked him up in her arms and cradled him. Warm against her breasts, leaking with milk."

Is What I'm Seeing Normal Postpartum Adjustment or Not?

Even without professional training, trust your observations. Knowing the mother beforehand allows you to notice even subtle changes that could be significant. Take a look at this checklist to familiarize yourself with the symptoms of postpartum depression.

A CHECKLIST TO GUIDE YOUR PARTNER, FRIENDS OR FAMILY IF THEY'RE CONCERNED

- *Crying daily for no real reason, lasting beyond a week*
- *Feeling anxious, can't sit still*
- *Feeling profound sadness*
- *Having panic attacks; racing heart, can't breathe*
- *Constantly worried about my baby's health or safety*
- *Not feeling connected to my baby or other people*
- *Feeling hopeless*
- *Unmotivated, I'm not taking care of my every day needs, i.e., brushing my teeth or washing my hair*
- *Unable to concentrate*
- *Afraid of being alone*
- *Confused*
- *Unable to sleep even though I am exhausted*
- *Unusually quiet, withdrawn, reclusive*
- *Exaggerated mood swings: feeling down to feeling too good*
- *Feeling guilty, unworthy*
- *Unable to control obsessive thoughts; talking incessantly*

AN ACT OF LOVE

The sooner a mother with postpartum depression receives treatment, the sooner she will be able to make a healthy postpartum transition. If she can't ask for help, make the phone call for her. If one doctor doesn't understand PPD, consult another one who does. Simple interventions, such as improving her diet or getting a few nights sleep, can make a big difference. Teach the baby to sleep through the night or care for the baby a few nights a week to allow the mother to sleep at least four consecutive hours, which will raise her seratonin levels—and this alone may improve or resolve her PPD. Sometimes, counseling helps to resolve issues surrounding her own mother-daughter relationship, clarify the role and expectations of motherhood, and integrate the "losses" becoming a mother has brought (e.g., changes in the marriage or career). Severe postpartum depression may be caused by chemical or hormonal imbalances and may require medication.

IF YOU HAVE ANY OF THE FOLLOWING, SEEK HELP IMMEDIATELY:

Suicidal fantasies • Fear of or fantasies of harming my baby • Experiencing bizarre thoughts or dreams

Postpartum Penny Game

Read: ***Birthing From Within,*** **pages 260-264**

A baby can and often does add a new element of harmony and closeness to a marriage, and can and often does give parents a new sense of purpose . . . But a baby rarely produces these changes quickly or painlessly.

The Penny Game assesses a couple's expectations and "transition-readiness." It was developed by Jay Belsky and John Kelly, authors of THE TRANSITION TO PARENTHOOD: HOW A FIRST CHILD CHANGES A MARRIAGE, as a tool to measure parents' expectations of themselves and each other during their transition from being a couple to becoming parents.

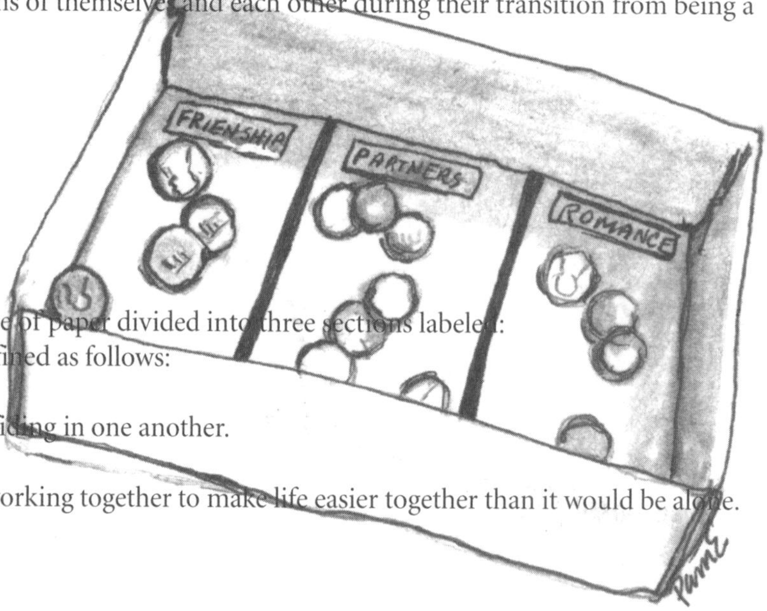

HERE'S HOW TO PLAY

First game

• Place fifteen pennies in a box or on a piece of paper divided into three sections labeled: Friendship, Partnership, and Romance, defined as follows:

Friendship: sharing mutual interests, confiding in one another.

Partnership: two people living together, working together to make life easier together than it would be alone.

Romance: physical attraction, intimacy.

• Distribute the pennies to each category in a way that best reflects the importance you are giving to the following areas since your baby was born. Jot down the penny distribution.

Friendship____________ **Partnership**____________ **Romance**____________

If you think or value the three components equally in your postpartum relationship, then put five pennies in each category.

Second Game:

First, divide the pennies to reflect how strongly you identified with the roles of Spouse, Worker, and Parent before your baby was born. Jot down the distribution:

Spouse____________ **Worker**____________ **Parent**____________

Now, divide the pennies to reflect how you see yourself now.

Spouse____________ **Worker**____________ **Parent**____________

Read Appendix C to gain more insight into your changing role-identity.

"Individuals who enter the transition with fewer idealistic (or what we usually referred to as romantic) expectations ('The baby will change my life and marriage') and fewer exaggerated ones ('He will change them tomorrow') are more likely to emerge from the transition happier about their marriages and their spouses than individuals who enter the starting gate wearing rose-colored glasses."

—Jay Belsky and John Kelly
The Transition to Parenthood

date ______________

. . . ____

One-sided expectations can be as threatening as unrealistic ones. If you are anticipating only one outcome (just like with birth plans) and the outcome is different, you will be inclined to seek fault and blame yourself or each other, or the baby!

Reflections On The Meaning of Marriage

The following gem from Joseph Campbell is excerpted from the transcripts of the six-hour PBS series, "The Power of Myth," a televised interview with Bill Moyers in 1986.

Marriage is "the reunion of the separated dyad. Originally you were one. You are now two in the world, but the recognition of the spiritual identity is what marriage is. It's different from a love affair. It has nothing to do with that. It's another mythological plane of experience. When people get married because they think it's a long-time love affair, they'll be divorced very soon, because all love affairs end in disappointment. But marriage is recognition of a spiritual identity. If we live a proper life, if our minds are on the right qualities in regarding the person of the opposite sex, we will find our proper male or female counterpart. But if we are distracted by certain sensual interests, we'll marry the wrong person. By marrying the right person, we reconstruct the image of the incarnate God, and that's what marriage is.

". . . if the marriage isn't a first priority in your life, you're not married. The marriage means the two that are one, the two become one flesh. If the marriage lasts long enough, and if you are acquiescing constantly to it instead of to individual personal whim, you come to realize that that is true—the two really are one.

". . . if the marriage isn't a first priority in your life, you're not married. The marriage means the two that are one, the two become one flesh. If the marriage lasts long enough, and if you are acquiescing constantly to it instead of to individual personal whim, you come to realize that that is true—the two really are one."

There are two completely different stages of marriage. First is the youthful marriage following the wonderful impulse that nature has given us in the interplay of the sexes biologically in order to produce children. But there comes a time when the child graduates from the family and the couple is left. I've been amazed at the number of my friends who in their forties or fifties go apart. They have had a perfectly decent life together with the child, but they interpreted their union in terms of their relationship through the child. They did not interpret it in terms of their own personal relationship to each other.

"Marriage is a relationship. When you make the sacrifice in marriage, you're sacrificing not to each other but to unity in a relationship. The Chinese image of the Tao, with the dark and light interacting—that's the relationship of yang and yin, male and female, which is what a marriage is. And that's what you have become when you have married. You're no longer this one alone; your identity is in a relationship. Marriage is not a simple love affair, it's an ordeal, and the ordeal is the sacrifice of ego to relationship in which two have become one."

During an unforgettable course I took with Braulio Montalvo, an internationally renown Family Therapist and consultant, I learned to envision marriage and family dynamics as a "structure."

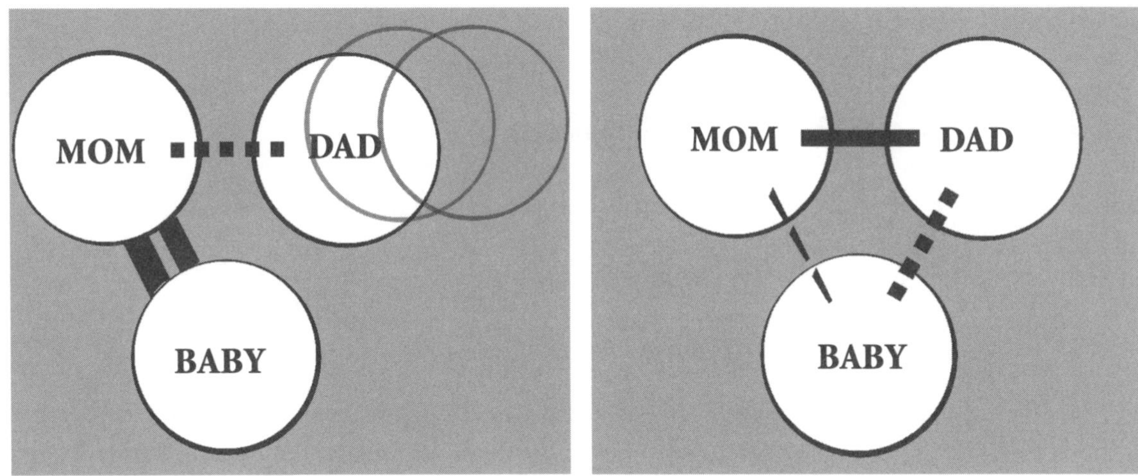

"[Our] research very clearly pointed to the fact that it was the couple's relationship, and not the relationship of one or the other parent to the child, that predicted the happiness and well-being of the family and ultimately of the child. But, parenting is a very lonely business the first year or so. It's very easy for couples to get out of touch."

—Philip Cowan
When Partners Become Parents

Write three to five simple things you could do every day that would require you to see, to listen to, to appreciate your partner. Simple acts of kindness or acknowledgement may restore and strengthen your bond during the transition to parenthood.

date ___________________

• • • ____

____

____

____

____

____

____

____

Six Bridge Builders

- "Surrender individual goals and needs in favor of working together as a team
- "Mothers and fathers merge individual selves into an "us" that has skills in conflict management
- "Resolve differences about differences of labor and work in a mutually satisfactory manner
- "Handle stresses in a way that does not overstress a partner or the marriage
- "Fight constructively and maintain a pool of common interests despite diverging priorities
- "Realize that however good a marriage becomes postbaby, it will not be as good in the same way it was pre-baby
- "Maintain the ability to communicate in a way that continues to nurture the marriage."

Jay Belsky and John Kelly
The Transition to Parenthood:
How a First Child Changes a Marriage

Our Baby's Temperament

ACTIVITY LEVEL

When you change your baby's diaper, does baby

a. lie quietly
b. kick and cry most of the time
c. wiggle and squirm

REGULARITY OF BIOLOGICAL FUNCTIONS i.e., eating, sleeping

Between midnight and 5 am, is your baby

a. asleep
b. awake three times or more
c. awake once or twice

ADAPTABILITY TO NEW SITUATIONS means how readily your baby to adjusts to new situations

When you take your baby to the supermarket, does baby

a. enjoy the trip and seem interested in changing environment
b. cry inconsolably until you return home
c. cry when you first enter the store, but then calm down with only occasional whimpers of complaint

RESPONSE TO NEW SITUATIONS OR PEOPLE

When a stranger comes toward your baby, does baby

a. smile and reach toward the person
b. pull away and scream until the stranger leaves
c. fuss and shy away

THRESHOLD OF SENSITIVITY i.e., intensity of stimuli needed to get a response

If the telephone rings while your baby is sleeping, will baby most likely

a. sleep through the noise
b. awaken instantly
c. whimper or cry out but then fall back to sleep

INTENSITY OF REACTION i.e., energy level of baby's response

When your baby is hungry, does baby

a. make sucking noises or suck fingers without much complaining
b. scream frantically before you have a chance to offer food
c. cry on and off until you offer food

DISTRACTIBILITY FROM AN ACTIVITY

If someone walks into the room while you're feeding your baby, does baby

a. continue feeding
b. stop and turn toward the noise
c. slow the sucking pace then continue feeding

QUALITY OF MOOD e.g., joyful or sad

During the course of the a day, does your baby spend most of her awake time

a. pleasantly
b. crying
c. showing no particular pattern

ATTENTION SPAN OR PERSISTENCE i.e., eagerness to return to a task

When your baby watches something over the crib, does baby

a. watch intently for an extended period
b. turn away looking for something else after only a few seconds
c. seem quite variable in attention

Now, turn to the next page to learn more about your baby's temperament.

In the 1950's, child development researchers Alexander Thomas and Stell Chess began a now famous 30-year longitudinal study out of New York University Medical Center. They followed 133 infants frombirth to adulthood and found that children do come equipped with their own unique personalities. The categories of temperamental characteristics make babies differ from each other. Circle the choices on this page that best describe your baby's personality. It might be interesting to score your baby separately, then compare notes.

Understanding Our Baby's Temperament

PARENTS ADD UP SCORES

How many "a," "b," and "c" responses?

_________"a"
_________"b"
_________"c"

FIVE OR MORE "A'S" SUGGEST AN "EASY" BABY

(40% were found to be in this category.)

Characteristics: Generally follow regular schedules, have a positive approach to change, and experience mild mood swings. "Easy" babies are "easy" for parents. Be aware: these kids respond slowly, which may concern doctors and teachers who may want to test for learning disabilities or neurological problems.

FIVE OR MORE "B'S" SUGGEST A DIFFICULT BABY

(10% of babies studied fell into this category.)

Characteristics: Displaying a single trait would not be considered difficult, but a combination of five or more makes it so. The stress parents of a "difficult" baby experience is brought about *by* (rather than the cause of) the baby's personality: Irregularity, withdrawal, negative moods, and intense reactions to stimuli or change. These parents need to realize having a "difficult" baby is not the result of their parenting skill (or perceived lack thereof), but that patience, and sometimes a little time away from the baby, may be needed to parent a "difficult" baby–especially during the first year.

FIVE OR MORE "C'S" POINT TO A "SLOW TO WARM-UP" PERSONALITY

(This category is 15% of babies studied.)

Characteristics: This baby often seems negative or cautious in new situations. Parents need to respond in kind by taking more time to introduce the baby to new situations, and be patient while the baby adjusts at his or her own, slower pace.

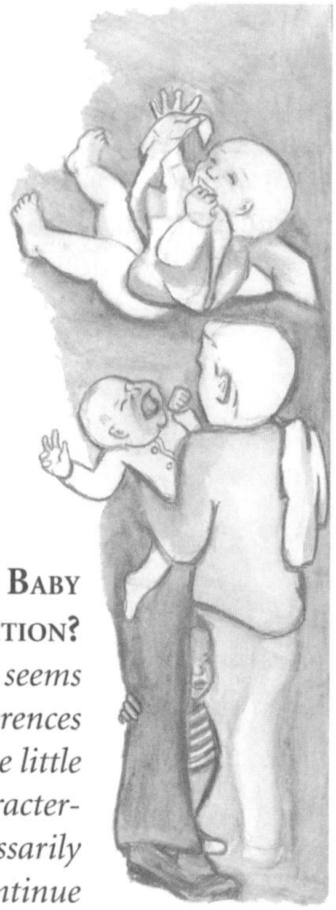

SO, FROM WHOM DID OUR BABY GET HIS OR HER DISPOSITION?

According to Thomas and Chess' study, it seems likely that temperament is inherited. Differences in personality types were shown to have little relationship to birth order. Personality characteristics present at birth are not necessarily unchanging, but patterns do often continue throughout the individual's life.

Mom: *How have your parents described your temperament as a baby?*

- *As a small child, do you remember what style of adult supervision or relating worked best for you?*
  - *How would they, or others, describe your overall temperament now? Did it change when you grew up?*
    - *How will knowing that personality is largely inherited affect the way you relate to your baby?*

date ______________

• • • ______________________________

Dad: *How have your parents described your temperament as a baby?*

- *How would they, or others, describe your overall temperament now? Did it change when you grew up?*
  - *As a small child, do you remember what style of adult supervision or relating worked best for you?*
    - *How might knowing that personality is largely inherited affect the way to relate to your baby?*

date ______________

• • • ______________________________

My Mommy and Daddy's Second Parent-Report Card

Now that you've had a little more experience, check your new report card.

Imagine your baby is evaluating you using a rating scale of "0" as the lowest possible "it ain't happenin'" score, 4-ish for "good job"— to "7" for achieving "excellence."

Today's date:________________

BABY CARE BASICS	MOMMY	DADDY
Feeds me *(Dad gets full points for supporting breastfeeding)* **Diapers me** **Soothes me**		
BABY TALK LANGUAGE ARTS **Learned to interpret my cries** **Talks, coos, and sings to me**		
HOME ECONOMICS **Fulfills share of agreed upon household chores** **Helps with grocery shopping & cooking** **Responds realistically to changes in finances** **Help each other without having to beg**		
CO-PARENTING SOCIAL SKILLS **Play well together (quality and frequency of fun time)** **Helps my other parent "Follow Their Bliss"** **Tries to understand my other parent's point of view**		
RELATING TO MY GRANDPARENTS **Open to accepting good advice and assistance** **Able to set necessary boundaries** **Allows my grandparents to do their job, i.e., spoil me**		
TOTALS		

Parent-Babysitting Co-ops

SUGGESTED GUIDELINES FOR ORGANIZING AND MAINTAINING A BABYSITTING CO-OP

1. Form a group of four to eight mothers/couples with a potential for cohesiveness, friendship, trust, and who live in relatively close proximity. Schedule an initial planning meeting, then meet every so often (i.e., every three months) to keep abreast of changes, problems, and to maintain group cohesiveness.

2. At first meeting, each parent/couple is given 20 hours worth of time-tokens; conceivably 15 one-hour tokens and 20 quarter-hour tokens. Tokens can be checkers, cards, or bottle caps. Babysitting time is calculated to the next quarter hour, e.g., 7:00 to 9:08 pm would be 2.25 hours.

3. Some Co-ops charge one token **per child** per hour.

4. The families decide whether the child goes to the Parent-Sitter(s') home or the Parent-Sitter(s) come to the baby/child's home.

5. The Parent-Babysitter(s) are "paid" from the time you arrive (even if you do not go out immediately) to the time you actually leave their home (unless you have mutually agreed to visit). Honoring this agreement is the key to avoiding feelings of your being taken advantage of or burdened.

6. Daytime and evenings are paid at a "straight-time" rate. Sitting after a specified time, say midnight, or on a holiday, is time-and-a-half (unless otherwise agreed upon).

7. Either parent or the couple may babysit.

8. Likewise, if there is illness in the home of the Parent-Sitter, the sitter should notify the parents in advance, giving as much warning as possible so other arrangements might be made.

9. If a parent/couple collects more than 30 hours worth of tokens, they should refrain from accepting more invitations to babysit until she/they have spent a few tokens. Be mindful not to get below eight tokens for any length of time. If you find yourself in either of these situations much of the time, consider whether the Babysitting Co-op is not working for you, or you are not working with the Co-op. Be aware: If any member(s) are too active or not active enough in the Co-op, all members suffer.

10. Whenever your supply of tokens is dwindling, let the other parents in the Co-op know that you want to be called to sit.

11. During the initial organization meeting, all parents mutually agree on what is expected, acceptable, and the "limits of care." For example: Is TV allowed? Is it okay to take another child in the car on errands?

Creating a Parent-Led Postpartum Support Group

"It has been said that there are two kinds of friends, friends of time and friends of like mind. The first—pals from the old neighborhood, summer camp, our first job—give our lives continuity, the second—soul mates who share our interests, values, goals—give our lives possibility. Both stir our capacity to care and connect, or as the writer Anais Nin once said, 'Each friend represents a world in us, a world possibly not born until they arrive.'"

OPRAH MAGAZINE, AUGUST 2001

BEGIN WITH A BRAINSTORMING SESSION

New parents often find the best source of emotional and practical support is from other new parents who are still "in the trenches." Gather together to work out the ground rules for your group using the following exploratory questions.

- How often do we want to meet?
- How much time do we want to spend at each get-together?
- Propose times (day or evening), and day of the week.
- Where should we meet? Would we prefer outings in different places (i.e., parks, the zoo) or to rotate meeting in our homes?
- What is the purpose and structure of our group? Do we want our get-together to be purely social, semi-educational or have some other theme?
- What would keep me interested and committed to this group?
- How many parents do we want in our group? How will we add new members if some of us drop out or move?

SUGGESTIONS FOR FINDING NEW MOTHERS (AND FATHERS) FOR OUR SUPPORT GROUP

- *Parents from childbirth class*
- *Nursing support groups*
- *Advertise in community newspapers or newsletters*

A SUMMARY OF OUR POSTPARTUM SUPPORT GROUP AGREEMENTS

Notes & Personal Reflections

date ________________

. . . ____________________

SECTION • NINE

Preserving Memories of Your Pregnancy & Birth

"Our story is of moments when even slow motion moved too fast for the shutter of the camera"

—Adrienne Rich

Highlights & Favorite Memories of Our Childbirth Class

date ______________

. . . ______________________________

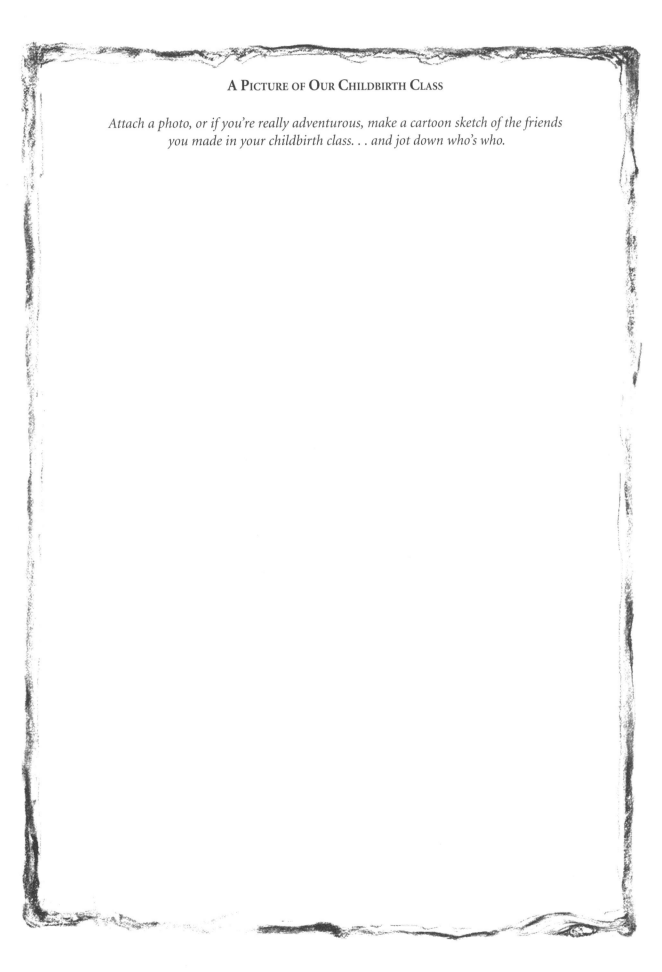

A Picture of Our Childbirth Class

Attach a photo, or if you're really adventurous, make a cartoon sketch of the friends you made in your childbirth class. . . and jot down who's who.

Our Birth Story

There are moments lived during labor and birth that will be burned into your memory forever. Soon after birth, however, some thoughts, images, and feelings will begin to fade. The longer you wait, the more you will forget. Even if you are exhausted, overwhelmed and busy, begin jotting down and sketching images within a few days or weeks after the birth.

If you gave birth under general anesthesia or can't remember a part of the labor, ask someone who was there to fill you in. Ask him or her to be objective, to tell you what happened (not necessarily their experience or opinion of it).

Write (or draw) whatever comes to mind; write the story from your perspective—remember: this is not a mini-medical report. Don't edit (in your head or on the paper)—just write! Keep writing through laughter or tears. This heartfelt account written in your own hand will be a treasured heirloom in the years to come.

date ____________

. . . ____________

Our Birth Story, continued . . .

Our Birth Story, continued . . .

Our Baby's First Moments

Read: ***Birthing From Within,*** **pages 173-176**

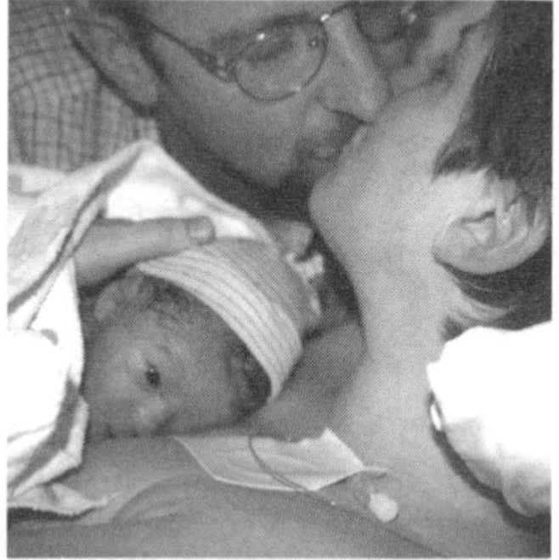

photo: Palmer Scheutzow

"For by his face straight shall you know his heart."
—William Shakespeare
Richard III

Show me your original face" is a *koan* a Zen teacher might give to a student, and, it's what every baby does for its parents moments after his or her birth. Parents are blessed when they see the original face of their newborn child. You may see your baby's character or family traits in its first expression—a face permanently imprinted in your heart—and a lifelong reminder of who your child truly is.

As best you can, put in words, a poem or a song, what you experienced looking into your baby's eyes for the first time. Sometimes a picture truly is worth a thousand words, and a sketch of that moment will capture the feeling best.

SEEING OUR BABY FOR THE FIRST TIME

date ________________

• • • ____

A Treasured Moment of the Day Our Baby Was Born

When you recall the events of the day your baby was born, there is a special moment you want to remember. Preserve this memory through journaling and drawing; include lots of details, such as the light in the room, or the moment you gathered up strength and determination in labor.

date ____________________

. . . ______________________________

A Memorable Moment of the Day Our Baby Was Born

Our Family & Friends' Memories of Our Birth

DEAR FAMILY, FRIENDS, AND BIRTH ATTENDANTS,

Our new family and future generations will treasure every anecdote recorded about the day __________________was born. Please, enrich our journal by writing a note in one of the "quilt squares." Write about your own birth-as-a grandparent/ aunt/ uncle/ sibling, write about an unforgettable moment, or pen your special wish for the little one. Sign your full name and note your relationship to us or our baby.

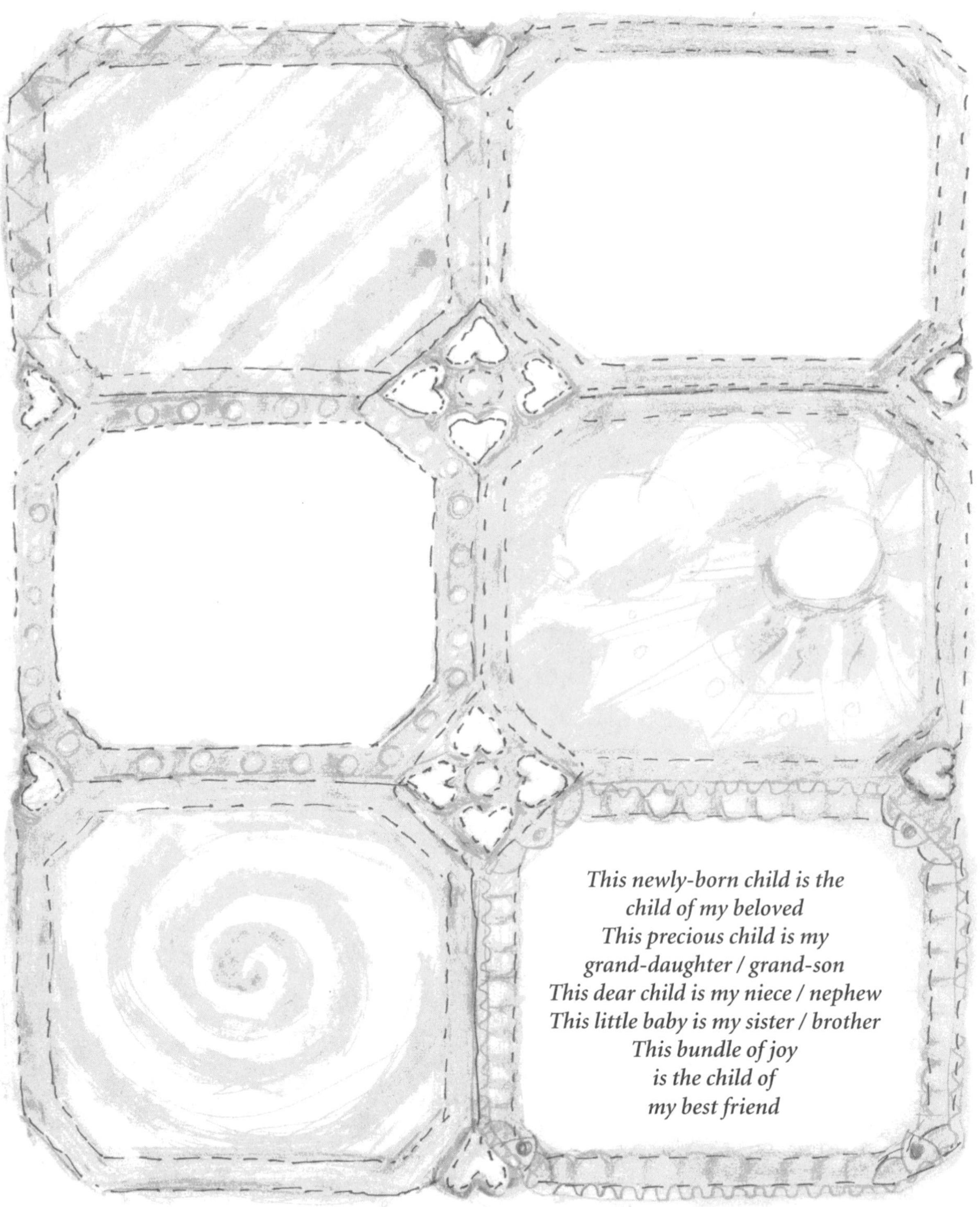

This newly-born child is the
child of my beloved
This precious child is my
grand-daughter / grand-son
This dear child is my niece / nephew
This little baby is my sister / brother
This bundle of joy
is the child of
my best friend

Announcing My "Birth" as a Parent

Along with your Baby-Birth Announcements, make a Parent-Birth Announcement that describes *your* "birth" as a parent! You could send your announcement to someone in your family and closest friends, or make it just for you and preserve it in this journal.

HOW TO MAKE A PARENT-BIRTH ANNOUNCEMENT

When making your Parent-Birth Announcement follow the traditionally concise design of baby-birth announcements which "list" the baby's name, birth date, time of arrival, weight and length, and often include a photo. A parent-birth announcement isn't a detailed narrative of the labor but, like a baby-birth announcement, provides brief declarations portraying your labor, such as its "length" or a personal victory and transformation you are experiencing.

Take inspiration from the following ideas, choose three or four that appeal to you, and begin creating your parent-birth announcement.

- *Length of labor*
- *Something I did in labor that worked, surprised me, or was outrageous for me*
- *What I now know about myself that I didn't know before labor*
- *What I now know about the universe that I didn't know before I became a parent*
- *The moment I realized "I am a mother" or "I am a father" (this moment might have been the moment of birth, a few hours or even days later)*
- *How giving birth and becoming a parent has changed me?*

Your Parent-Birth Announcement can be plain, practical or outrageously creative; it can be hand-made or computer generated. Add photos, drawings, ribbons, a collage of cut-outs from magazines or cards, etc. You can make one together, or each make your own.

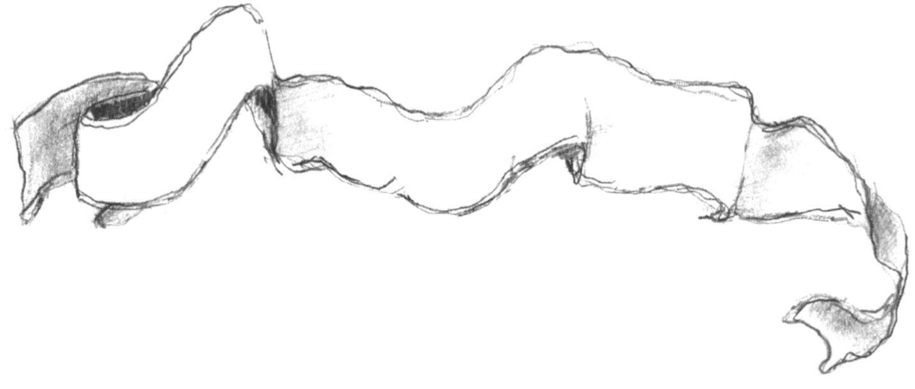

Attach your
Parent-Birth Announcement
&
Baby-Birth Announcement
here

Drawing My Baby

When my boys were babies and toddlers, I absently made many sketches of them in my journals as they nursed or napped. When they were much older I was delighted to discover these forgotten sketches—they brought back memories and feelings that could not have been expressed in words.

You do not need to be an experienced artist to draw your baby, *and it doesn't matter if the drawing resembles your baby. The beauty of drawing your baby is that you have to sit awhile with your baby, you have to really look at your baby, and as you draw, you really 'see' your baby.*

PAM ENGLAND

ART SUPPLIES:

Soft charcoal pencils, soft lead (number two) pencils, or my personal favorite, Conte pencils or sticks. All of these are "forgiving," i.e., they make light lines that are easy to rub away or erase, and fun to rub into shadows.

A paper smudge stick for soft shading and blending

Rubber eraser that doesn't make the paper raw after erasing

Many of the following tips and illustrations were extracted or adapted from Judy Clifford's article, "DRAWING YOUR BABY" (MOTHERING MAGAZINE, SUMMER 1991). You will "see" your baby by drawing your baby, even if the drawing doesn't resemble him or her at all. Most importantly, when you see your drawing later, because you had to spend more time and more fully enter the moment to draw it than to take a snapshot, it may invoke deeper feelings and memories than most photos - mine do!

BEFORE YOU DRAW – SEE

For 60 years, one of America's most beloved artists, Norman Rockwell, painted ordinary people in everyday happenings in average America. His description of how to pose and paint a chicken was remarkably similar to my own experience of trying to draw my children (especially Luc).

> *"You pick up the chicken and rock him back and forth a few times. When you set him down he will stand just as you've placed him for four or five minutes. Of course you have to run behind the easel pretty quickly to do much painting before the chicken moves. But it's better than trying to paint him while he's dashing about the studio . . . It's very strenuous painting a chicken."*

Drawing a moving target might discourage you. One way to begin drawing your baby is while he/she is asleep. Another is to begin the drawing from a photograph, but add the finishing touches while looking at your baby—to capture the essence of your baby's gestures and nature.

Let your gaze softly penetrate the surface of your baby; see the blended, moving colors, shadows, textures. Begin to see his or her body as connected geometric shapes. For example, when you look at your child's head, see an oval, an egg-shape; looking at the trunk of its body you might see an oval or a rounded rectangle; plump baby shoulders are soft, rounded circles; arms are formed by connecting two elongated ovals.

Take a Visual Tour of Your Baby's Face

Human faces are interesting to study and to draw. You might prefer to draw your baby's hand, or its feet. Although I am focusing on offering tips for drawing your baby's face, the following principles apply to all body parts.

Proportion

Notice that your baby's face occupies much less space on its head (a ratio of about one to three), than does an adult's (a ratio of about one to two). While drawing your baby, be sure to allow for sufficient volume at the back of the head.

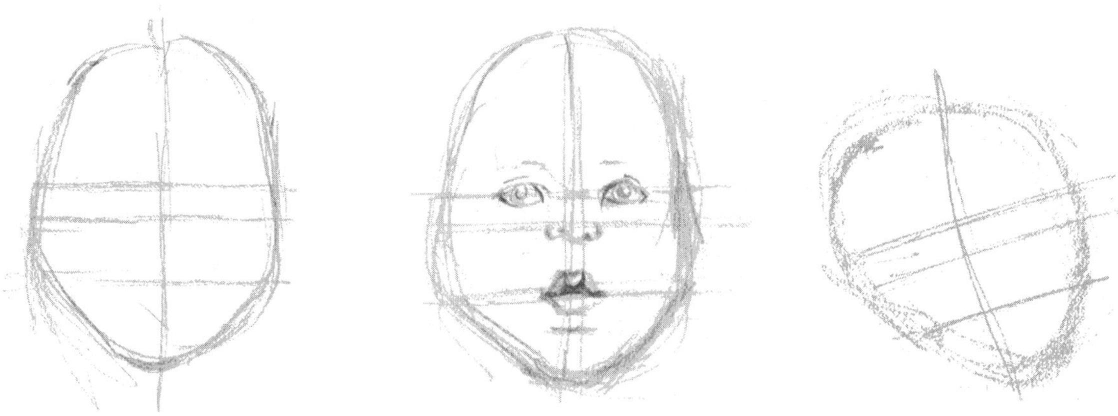

Imagine a Grid Overlaying the Subject

An imaginary grid allows you to study the relative distance between, and the alignment of, various parts of your baby's body. The tops of the eye sockets, for example, line up with the tops of the ears; the top of the mouth aligns with the bottoms of the ears. Babies eyes are set further apart than adults; and because babies lack a developed brow, the area between the eyes is relatively flat.

What is the shape of your baby's eyes?

"The inside corner of each eye is aligned vertically with the outer edge of each nostril. The opening between the upper and lower eyelids is neither symmetrical and almond-like nor circular; it really has a shape of its own."

What is the shape of your baby's nose?

"Notice that the baby's nose is a continuation of the forehead, and reveals no evidence of a brow line. An infant's nose is broader and flatter than an adult's —its tip is closer to the face; and its base is wider, in proportion to the mouth and chin. The nostril cavities at the base of the nose form a triangle with the tip of the nose, which is flattened at the top."

What is the shape of your baby's mouth?

Take a look. "In reality, the mouth extends forward from just under the nose, and reaches all the way down to the chin. The entire area extends forward in a barrel like protrusion. The bottom edge of the lower lip sits about halfway between the bottom of the nose and the bottom of the chin."

Where are your baby's ears in relation to the face?

The ears lie within the space formed by one imaginary line extending across the top of the eyelids and another extending across the top of the mouth. An infant's ears are usually quite large and about twice as long as they are wide.

NOW IT'S TIME TO DRAW YOUR BABY

Begin by lightly sketching the outline and shapes. Draw loosely connected lines to suggest the shapes of various structures. Then lightly shade the drawing to separate the light and dark places. As a final step, add details and color.

AVOID THESE COMMON & FRUSTRATING PITFALLS

- Don't draw firm, final lines in the beginning stages of the drawing, because then every line would have to be just right—or erased and erased! Also, begin with an overall sketch outlining the whole face or body, sketching in lines for important features.
- Next, sketch the overall shape of the face as a slightly elongated circle or egg shaped
- Then, lightly sketch four lines to guide your placement of the baby's eyes, nose, and mouth:

1. A line that divides this ovoid shape in half vertically (from crown to chin)
2. Another horizontally through the center (where you will draw the eyes)
3. Below the line for the eyes and slightly more than halfway to the bottom of the oval shape, sketch another line—marking where you will draw the center of the mouth
4. Finally, a line about a third of the distance from the "eye line," marking where the tip of the nose will go.

Don't build a face by drawing first the eyes, then adding the nose— because you will not be able to keep the features in proportion or relationship to one another.

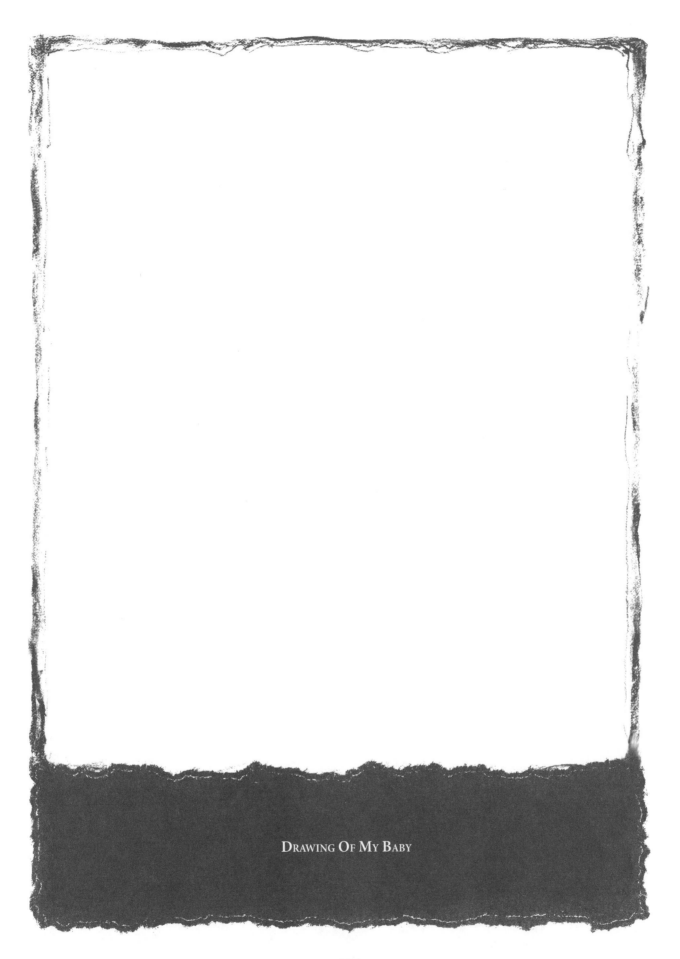
DRAWING OF MY BABY

Notes & Personal Reflections

date ______________

. . . ______________

date ______________

• • • ______________

First Month

date ____________

. . . ____________

MILESTONES & MEMORABLE MOMENTS OF OUR

Second Month

date ______________

. . . ______________

MILESTONES & MEMORABLE MONTHS OF OUR

Third Month

date ______________

• • • ______________

MILESTONES & MEMORABLE MOMENTS OF OUR

Fourth Month

date ____________________

. . . ____________________

MILESTONES & MEMORABLE MOMENTS OF OUR

Fifth Month

date ________________

. . .

MILESTONES & MEMORABLE MOMENTS OF OUR

Sixth Month

date ____________

. . . ____________

MILESTONES & MEMORABLE MOMENTS OF OUR

Seventh Month

date ____________

. . . ____________

MILESTONES & MEMORABLE MOMENTS OF OUR

Eighth Month

date ____________________

• • • ____________________

MILESTONES & MEMORABLE MOMENTS OF OUR

Ninth Month

date ______________

. . . ______________

MILESTONES & MEMORABLE MOMENTS OF OUR

Tenth Month

date ____________________

. . . ____

MILESTONES & MEMORABLE MOMENTS OF OUR

Eleventh Month

date ____________

. . . ____________

Twelfth Month

date ______________

. . . ______________

Reflections on Our First Year

"The day your baby was born your life was changed more than you ever dreamed. You found you had sprouted invisible antennae that picked up every alteration in breathing, every variation in temperature, every nuance of expression in your tiny daughter. No one told you that the change was irreversible. That you would feel in your own heart every pain, every loss, every disappointment, every rebuff, every cruelty that she experiences—life long."

–Roseanne Ambrose-Brown

I was deeply touched by a line in a note Peggy O'Mara, editor of Mothering magazine, sent me on my first-born's first birthday—it read, "bittersweet, isn't it?" Yes, it was, but I did not expect it to be. Sky's first birthday was also *my* first birthday as a parent. From morning 'til night, I re-lived our birth-day a year ago, and reflected on "bad-mommy" and "brilliant-mommy" moments, and special events that highlighted the year-long rocky and magical transition to parenthood.

Today, recap and write the bitter and the sweet highlights of your first year:

date ______________

. . . ____

date ___________

• • • ___________

How We Celebrated Our Baby's First Birthday

Set aside special time to celebrate your first birthday as a parent.

Begin this day by waking in awareness. Perhaps you can ask a friend to give you the gift of breakfast in bed or of drawing you a rose petal bubble bath.

date ____________________

. . . ____

Write or draw yourself a First Parent-Birthday message

date ___________________

• • • ___________________

World and Local News the Day You Turned One:

date ______________

. . . ______________

SECTION • TEN

Appendices

APPENDIX A

Looking At, Listening To & Learning From My Birth Art

Before talking about or exploring what you've made, take a moment to sit back and take in what has come out of you—into the light—so you could see it and learn from it.

These questions are not in any particular order; go with whichever ones apply.

LOOKING INTO FEELING THE IMAGE

- What was I feeling when I made this birth art? When I look at it now, what am I feeling? Where do I feel that in my body?

- Is there a story, a time, or place, behind this drawing? Is this the beginning, middle, or end of the story?

- Ask yourself, "If this character or symbol could speak, what would it be saying to me?" You might want to jot down what first comes up.

- Does anything in this image surprise me?

- Is there anything that doesn't make sense to me?

- Is anything missing in the drawing? If so, go a little deeper. What does that missing part symbolize/represent in my life? Is that missing in my life?

LET THE SYMBOLS DO THE TALKING

Before you could read a book, you had to learn to read letters and how their combinations formed words that represent feelings, experiences, or concepts. In the same way, every thing and every character in art is a symbol that represents a feeling, experience, or idea.

Here's an easy way to translate symbols into words.

- Choose a character or symbol in your drawing that intrigues you (it could be inanimate, e.g., a chair or bed; a person or the "role" the person is playing in the drawing, e.g., "midwife").

- Then, continue to dialogue with the symbol. What does it know, or want you to know or do?

WHAT IS YOUR BIRTH ART TEACHING YOU?

- As a result of making this drawing, what do you now know—that you didn't know before?

- Because you know this, what will you do differently now?

APPENDIX B

Creating a Space That Will Help Me Open

(from pages 124-125)

PART ONE: PRIMORDIAL, INSTINCTIVE ENVIRONMENTAL NEEDS

- Privacy, Nest, Few distractions
- Warmth
- Dim light
- Water, Nourishment

If you wrote "safety" on your list, be aware that safety is a concept; "safety" is not something you can *do* in labor. Be more specific, ask yourself "What would I do or want as part of my birth space to make my labor-environment feel safe?"

Respectively keep in mind that a labor room that is cold, brightly lit, with ringing telephones, or occupied by anyone who is *watching* you or with whom you feel self-conscious or guarded in any way, will cause a natural release of adrenalin (which allows you to shiver to keep warm in a cold room, or be alert, "fight or flight" or run to a safer place). Adrenalin in labor neutralizes oxytocin, the hormone that makes the uterine muscle rhythmically contract to squeeze your baby out.

Think of a conducive birth space this way: The same environment that got your baby *in* there is the kind of environment you need to get it *out*. So if bright lights, answering the phone, listening to people talking to and over you, worked for you on the way "in"— then it might work in labor. Otherwise, create a loving space in labor as best you can.

PART TWO: THE MODERN BIRTH SPACE

Key words or phrases like:

- Shower
- Aromatherapy
- Massage
- Your Baby's Name or Fetal Name
- Drumming CD

My Daily Mindfulness Practice-Journal

The results are visibly distinct when one lifts weights three times a week in contrast to only once a month.

Practicing mindfulness is an empowering ritual of preparation. Creating a new habit requires repetition for 21 consecutive days. Daily reflection and journaling in this section of your KEEPSAKE JOURNAL will keep you focused on practice until mindfulness becomes automatic.

There are no guarantees how any of the techniques or practices you learn from the BIRTHING FROM WITHIN book or class will work for you in labor—and you don't want to be outcome-focused anyway. But practicing mindfulness in your everyday life builds a mindset, a way of being aware and focused. After a while, living-in-awareness will become natural for you; in labor you'll just do more of it and with greater concentration and motivation.

Learning comes from both success and failure. Choose a quiet time each day to enter what you learned, problems encountered during practice, or questions that came up. Here's an example:

Today, I practiced: *Non-focused Awareness and Living Question*
in the ___AM _*X*_Mid-day ___PM ___Forgot

Notes on what I learned or want to ask about in class:

When I ask myself, **"How am I asking for what I need in this moment?"** *I come face-to-face with how difficult it is for me to ask for anything. But I happily discovered when I do ask, nobody blinks an eye and they usually give me what I want.*

PRACTICING
MINDFULNESS
IS AN **EMPOWERING**
RITUAL
OF ***PREPARATION***

Date: ________________ Today, I practiced: ______________________________

in the ___AM ___Mid-day ___PM ___Forgot

Notes on what I learned or want to ask about in class: ______________________

Date: ________________ Today, I practiced: ______________________________

in the ___AM ___Mid-day ___PM ___Forgot

Notes on what I learned or want to ask about in class: ______________________

Date: ________________ Today, I practiced: ______________________________

in the ___AM ___Mid-day ___PM ___Forgot

Notes on what I learned or want to ask about in class: ______________________

Date: ________________ Today, I practiced: ______________________________

in the ___AM ___Mid-day ___PM ___Forgot

Notes on what I learned or want to ask about in class: ______________________

Date: ________________ Today, I practiced: ______________________________

in the ___AM ___Mid-day ___PM ___Forgot

Notes on what I learned or want to ask about in class: ______________________

Date: ________________ Today, I practiced: ______________________________

in the ___AM ___Mid-day ___PM ___Forgot

Notes on what I learned or want to ask about in class: ______________________

Date: ________________ Today, I practiced: ______________________________

in the ___AM ___Mid-day ___PM ___Forgot

Notes on what I learned or want to ask about in class: ______________________

Date: ____________________ Today, I practiced: ____________________
in the ___AM ___Mid-day ___PM ___Forgot
Notes on what I learned or want to ask about in class: ____________________

Date: ____________________ Today, I practiced: ____________________
in the ___AM ___Mid-day ___PM ___Forgot
Notes on what I learned or want to ask about in class: ____________________

Date: ____________________ Today, I practiced: ____________________
in the ___AM ___Mid-day ___PM ___Forgot
Notes on what I learned or want to ask about in class: ____________________

Date: ____________________ Today, I practiced: ____________________
in the ___AM ___Mid-day ___PM ___Forgot
Notes on what I learned or want to ask about in class: ____________________

Date: ____________________ Today, I practiced: ____________________
in the ___AM ___Mid-day ___PM ___Forgot
Notes on what I learned or want to ask about in class: ____________________

Date: ____________________ Today, I practiced: ____________________
in the ___AM ___Mid-day ___PM ___Forgot
Notes on what I learned or want to ask about in class: ____________________

Date: ____________________ Today, I practiced: ____________________
in the ___AM ___Mid-day ___PM ___Forgot
Notes on what I learned or want to ask about in class: ____________________

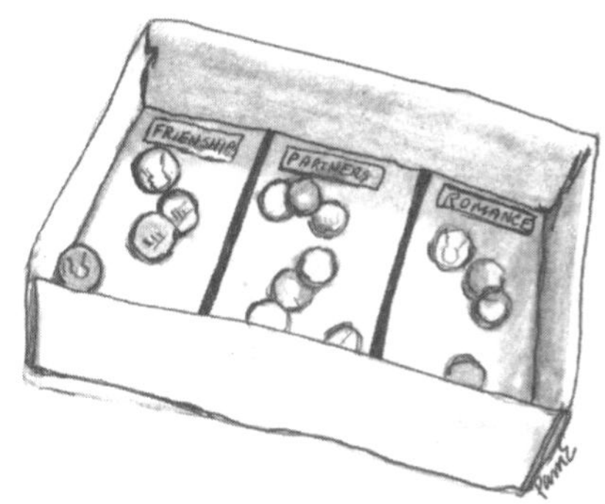

More Insights From the Penny Game

GAME ONE

In their study on couple's transition to parenthood, Belsky and Kelly observed that the average participant scored the Penny Game as follows: six for Friendship; four for Partnership; five for Romance. An ideal score—one that reflected transition-worthy expectations—is: seven for Friendship; five for Partnership; three for Romance."

> *"While [parents] expected the baby to bring a good many relatively realistic things, they didn't expect that along with the good he also would bring some bad in the form of exhaustion, unsatisfying sex, and a host of other common transition-time complaints. During the transition, such one-sided expectations can be as threatening to marital happiness as wildly unrealistic ones. When a couple anticipates only the good, they assume it must be someone's fault when they encounter the bad. So instead of taking the bad in stride as do parents who see trouble and strife as an inevitable part of the transition, they begin pointing fingers—sometimes at the marriage, sometimes at themselves, and sometimes even at the child."*

GAME TWO: THE ROLES OF SPOUSE, WORKER AND PARENT

At the start of the transition, women allotted almost as many pennies as men to the Worker Role, which is to say that mothers-to-be were almost as likely as fathers-to-be to identify themselves as workers. But after the baby's birth a divergence developed. Women (including working women) began allotting more and more of their pennies to the parenting role, while men gave more to the worker role.

> *"Most of the disagreements new mothers and fathers have about expenses arise from another difference between members of the His and Hers transition: Parenting changes men's and women's self-perceptions in very different ways. . . The different forms of economic logic that new mothers and fathers develop arise from this divergence in self-perception? Many a man's thinking about money issues is dominated by his worker impulse to conserve and enhance financial resources. A new father frequently works longer hours to increase income and begins cutting back on his own consumption. Now he shuts off the lights when he leaves a room and brings a sandwich to work instead of eating lunch out.*
>
> *Many a woman's logic is often shaped by her close identification with the parenting role. New mothers also turn out lights and 'brown-bag it' to save money. However, because a mother sees herself first and foremost as a nurturer, the woman's chief concern becomes the baby's well-being. And this often produces economic choices that put her in conflict with her conservation-minded husband."*

(An example was offered of a mother wanting to baby proof the living-room windows with sliding metal guards, but the father did not think the windows would pose a hazard until their child was two or three years old.)